EBA

A QUARK FOR MISTER MARK

A QUARK FOR MISTER MARK

101 Poems about Science

edited by
Maurice Riordan
and Jon Turney

faber and faber

First published in 2000
by Faber and Faber Limited
3 Queen Square London WC1N 3AU

Photoset by Wilmaset Ltd, Wirral
Printed in England by
MPG Books Ltd, Bodmin, Cornwall

The right of Maurice Riordan and Jon Turney to be identified as editors
of this work has been asserted in accordance with Section 77
of the Copyright, Designs and Patents Act 1988

A CIP record for this book
is available from the British Library

ISBN 0-571-20542-9

2 4 6 8 10 9 7 5 3 1

The wandering earth herself may be
Only a sudden flaming word,
In clanging space a moment heard,
Troubling the endless reverie

W. B. Yeats

Contents

[vii]

[ix]

[x]

Introduction

People have been noticing science more lately. This isn't surprising. There's a lot of it about. The sheer amount of science produced in the last hundred years, and the way it has affected everyday life, has no precedent. And poets, who ought to be good at noticing things, have noticed too.

Not all of them, of course. But enough to give plenty to choose from for an anthology like this. We first started to notice and collect the poems here a few years ago. There was nothing premeditated about this. Simply we – one a writer about science who reads poetry for pleasure, one a poet who happens to be interested in science – found we were coming across more responses to science and scientific ideas in contemporary poems.

The idea of introducing them all to each other in one book grew out of conversations about what we were finding. The motive, simply pleasure. So there is no intent here to take stock of writers' views of science, no aim to be comprehensive, certainly no wish to feed readers science under the guise of poetry.

Just as well, because the 101 pieces here are not, of course, strictly about science. They are about love and death, frailty, grief, mischief, moments of recollection and introspection, about the sorts of things one expects to find in poems anyway. Science may cast such themes in a different light, but its use in poetry is often oblique, glancing, wry or sardonic, or it is so much a part of a way of seeing that the reader, and even the writer, may not be conscious of its presence. Even poets whose work is suffused with scientific vocabulary and metaphor, like Alice Fulton, comment directly on science only rarely.

But one such comment by her appears within, and another almost made the final cut. The more rather than less direct treatment was one thing we were looking for when we had to move from the pleasant business of stacking up poems to the more regretful stage of setting most of them aside. Even so, some of the comments, like Peter Redgrove's 'In the Lab with the Lady Doctor', are very indirect indeed. Another rule which we made and then enjoyed breaking was to stick with English-language originals – though two of the exceptions, Hans-Magnus Enzensberger and Miroslav Holub, work closely with their translators, and so their poems could be regarded as 'naturalized' in English. And then the splendid example of Dryden's version of the Discourse of Pythagoras, from Ovid, reminds us that the distinction between translated and original poems is hard to maintain.

We have included a number of well-known poets from the past, where they have offered intriguing companions for newer work, suggesting surprising contrasts or continuities or, perhaps, that there is little new under the sun. And we have wanted too to retrieve some poets who are now almost forgotten – like Anna Laetitia Barbauld, one of several women poets of the seventeenth and eighteenth centuries who turned to science with enthusiasm.

But we do lean towards the contemporary. This not because of any craving for novelty, but it is where we came in. Ever since John Heath-Stubbs and Phillips Salman's pioneering and historically oriented *Poems of Science* appeared in 1984, there has been a wealth of new writing which meets our rather inclusive criteria. Much of it has been in the USA and is generously represented in another, more recent, collection, *Verse and Universe* (1998), edited by Kurt Brown. This nicely complements our own preference, which was to cast as wide a net as we could. That said, there is only one real reason for each of the pieces here: because we like them. When in doubt, we insisted that we both like them, and almost all pass that test.

Although others are free to invent them – that is part of the fun of anthologies – we will deny that this little book embodies any grand thesis or major claim beyond the fact that the filter we applied yields a surprising view. There is a good deal of talk these days about relations between science and arts, but mostly scientists and artists are best left to do their own thing. The traffic between science and art is, in any case, almost always one-way. The notion that there is any deep relation between artistic and scientific creativity is belied by the fact that there are vanishingly few distinguished practitioners of both. We are pleased that a few scientists appear here – but the chemist Roald Hoffman, Alex Comfort and Holub are the only three of professional distinction. The rest are all poets whose intellectual curiosity extends in varying degrees to the sciences.

We did find, though, that poets' curiosity has its blind spots. Or perhaps only certain kinds of news from science can get through clearly. The scale and age of the universe impress plenty of poets, and one could make a sizeable, but repetitive, collection just featuring awe-struck or morose meditations on star-gazing. The struggle to understand evolution is another, nineteenth-century, theme which continues to thrive, perhaps because it builds on a traditional poetic concern with natural history. Poets are good, it seems, on heavenly bodies and lower life forms. But there are areas of science that hardly get a look in. And, although our definition of science is inclusive, we found rather little to read about technology, though Peter Redgrove again comes to the rescue.

Still, we are tracking a moving target. The cascade of popular science books which have entertained readers of non-fiction in the last couple of decades shows no signs of thinning out, and they are catching the attention of poets as well as other artists. There are already lots of poems about the preoccupations of those books – cosmology, consciousness, computers and chaos theory – although not so many of great merit. And we are aware of an ongoing story. Even as we put the book together, we found eligible poems appearing in magazines and new collections to unsettle our consensus. Perhaps we will soon be reading more poems which exploit the vocabularies or concepts of plate tectonics, neuroscience or software engineering. Science promises great things in the new century, and no doubt poets will continue to engage with new as well as old science. Meantime, we hope you enjoy reading this selection from the poetic response to science thus far as much as we enjoyed making it.

A QUARK FOR MISTER MARK

On Looking up by Chance at the Constellations

You'll wait a long, long time for anything much
To happen in heaven beyond the floats of cloud
And the Northern Lights that run like tingling nerves.
The sun and moon get crossed, but they never touch,
Nor strike out fire from each other, nor crash out loud.
The planets seem to interfere in their curves,
But nothing ever happens, no harm is done.
We may as well go patiently on with our life,
And look elsewhere than to stars and moon and sun
For the shocks and changes we need to keep us sane.
It is true the longest drouth will end in rain,
The longest peace in China will end in strife.
Still it wouldn't reward the watcher to stay awake
In hopes of seeing the calm of heaven break
On his particular time and personal sight.
That calm seems certainly safe to last tonight.

After Reading a Child's Guide to Modern Physics

If all a top physicist knows
About the Truth be true,
Then, for all the so-and-so's,
Futility and grime,
Our common world contains,
We have a better time
Than the Greater Nebulae do,
Or the atoms in our brains.

Marriage is rarely bliss
But, surely it would be worse
As particles to pelt
At thousands of miles per sec
About a universe
In which a lover's kiss
Would either not be felt
Or break the loved one's neck.

Though the face at which I stare
While shaving it be cruel
For, year after year, it repels
An ageing suitor, it has,
Thank God, sufficient mass
To be altogether there,
Not an indeterminate gruel
Which is partly somewhere else.

Our eyes prefer to suppose
That a habitable place
Has a geocentric view,
That architects enclose

A quiet Euclidean space:
Exploded myths – but who
Would feel at home astraddle
An ever expanding saddle?

This passion of our kind
For the process of finding out
Is a fact one can hardly doubt,
But I would rejoice in it more
If I knew more clearly what
We wanted the knowledge for,
Felt certain still that the mind
Is free to know or not.

It has chosen once, it seems,
And whether our concern
For magnitude's extremes
Really becomes a creature
Who comes in a median size,
Or politicizing Nature
Be altogether wise,
Is something we shall learn.

'We want no dead weights on this expedition'

We want no dead weights on this expedition,
no credulous Charlies and no nervous Nellies.
Though not as hazardous as in the past
the intellectual skulls you see down there
all fell from this arête. So use some care –
look out and in, don't try to go too fast,
but climb, Goddamit, don't crawl on your bellies.

The particle physicist and the mathematician
I'll take. They're crazy, but they watch their feet.
I'll take one mystic – no, not you, Ouspensky,
nor you, Teilhard. You've got no head for heights.
What do you say, Sherpa? Very well, we'll take
two at the most – Eckhard and William Blake,
and watch it, you two – no religious fights.
I need a brain man, too (he's got the map
and the theodolite). You others, don't
for Christ's sake hold us up with poking for
the Absolute and Transcendent (you'll see plenty
of that keeping the rope taut, eyes front)
or any other Rosicrucian crap.
People who play games on this pass
end on a slab with parsley up their ass:
that was what put paid to those skulls down there.

Remember you've two feet, one left one right.
Now, if you're ready, we'll leave at zero twenty
that is, unless there are more fool suggestions.
The sherpa's name is Mi Pham. He's our guide.
Now, get those bloody packs on. Any questions?

[6]

from Orchestra

For that brave Sunne the Father of the Day,
Doth love this Earth, the Mother of the Night;
And like a revellour in rich aray,
Doth daunce his galliard in his lemman's sight,
Both back, and forth, and sidewaies, passing light;
    His princely grace doth so the gods amaze,
    That all stand still and at his beauty gaze.

But see the Earth, when he approcheth neere,
How she for joy doth spring and sweetly smile;
But see againe her sad and heavy cheere
When changing places he retires a while;
But those blake cloudes he shortly will exile,
    And make them all before his presence flye,
    As mists consum'd before his cheerefull eye.

Who doth not see the measures of the Moone,
Which thirteene times she daunceth every yeare?
And ends her pavine thirteene times as soone
As doth her brother, of whose golden haire
She borroweth part, and proudly doth it weare;
    Then doth she coyly turne her face aside,
    Then halfe her cheeke is scarse sometimes discride.

Next her, the pure, subtile, and clensing Fire
Is swiftly carried in a circle even;
Though Vulcan be pronounst by many a lyer,
The only halting god that dwels in heaven:
But that foule name may be more fitly given
    To your false Fire, that farre from heaven is fall:
    And doth consume, waste, spoile, disorder all.

[7]

And now behold your tender nurse the *Ayre*
And common neighbour that ay runns around;
How many pictures and impressions faire
Within her empty regions are there found;
Which to your sences Dauncing doe propound.
 For what are *Breath*, *Speech*, *Ecchos*, *Musicke*, *Winds*,
 But Dauncings of the Ayre in sundry kinds?

For when you breath, the *ayre* in order moves,
Now in, now out, in time and measure trew;
And when you speake, so well she dauncing loves,
That doubling oft, and oft redoubling new,
With thousand formes she doth her selfe endew
 For all the words that from our lips repaire
 Are nought but tricks and turnings of the ayre.

Hence is her pratling daughter *Eccho* borne,
That daunces to all voyces she can heare;
There is no sound so harsh that shee doth scorne,
Nor any time wherein shee wil forbeare
The ayrie pavement with her feet to weare;
 And yet her hearing sence is nothing quick,
 For after time she endeth every trick.

And thou sweet *Musicke*, Dauncing's onely life,
The eare's sole happinesse, the ayre's best speach;
Loadstone of fellowship, charming-rod of strife,
The soft mind's Paradice, the sicke mind's leach;
With thine own tong, thou trees and stons canst teach,
 That when the Aire doth dance her finest measure,
 Then art thou borne, the gods and mens sweet pleasure.

Lastly, where keepe the *Winds* their revelry,
Their violent turnings, and wild whirling hayes,
But in the Ayre's tralucent gallery?

[8]

Where shee herselfe is turnd a hundreth wayes,
While with those Maskers wantonly she playes;
    Yet in this misrule, they such rule embrace,
    As two at once encomber not the place.

If then fire, ayre, wandring and fixed lights
In every province of the imperiall skie,
Yeeld perfect formes of dauncing to your sights,
In vaine I teach the eare, that which the eye
With certaine view already doth descrie.
    But for your eyes perceive not all they see,
    In this I will your Senses master bee.

For loe the *Sea* that fleets about the Land,
And like a girdle clips her solide waist,
Musicke and measure both doth understand;
For his great chrystall eye is alwayes cast
Up to the Moone, and on her fixèd fast;
    And as she daunceth in her pallid spheere;
    So daunceth he about his Center heere.

Sometimes his proud greene waves in order set,
One after other flow unto the shore;
Which, when they have with many kisses wet,
They ebbe away in order as before;
And to make knowne his courtly love the more,
    He oft doth lay aside his three-forkt mace,
    And with his armes the timorous Earth embrace.

Onely the Earth doth stand for ever still:
Her rocks remove not, nor her mountaines meet:
(Although some wits enricht with Learning's skill
Say heav'n stands firme, and that the Earth doth fleet,
And swiftly turneth underneath their feet)

Yet though the Earth is ever stedfast seene,
On her broad breast hath Dauncing ever beene.

For those blew vaines that through her body spred,
Those saphire streames which from great hils do spring,
(The Earth's great duggs; for every wight is fed
With sweet fresh moisture from them issuing):
Observe a daunce in their wilde wandering;
    And still their daunce begets a murmur sweet,
    And still the murmur with the daunce doth meet.

Of all their wayes I love *Maeander*'s path,
Which to the tunes of dying swans doth daunce;
Such winding sleights, such turns and tricks he hath,
Such creeks, such wrenches, and such daliaunce;
That whether it be hap or heedlesse chaunce,
    In this indented course and wriggling play
    He seemes to daunce a perfect cunning *hay*.

But wherefore doe these streames for ever runne?
To keepe themselves for ever sweet and cleere:
For let their everlasting course be donne,
They straight corrupt and foule with mud appeare.
O yee sweet Nymphs that beautie's losse do feare,
    Contemne the drugs that Physicke doth devise,
    And learne of Love this dainty exercise.

See how those flowres that have sweet beauty too,
(The onely jewels that the Earth doth weare,
When the young Sunne in bravery her doth woo):
As oft as they the whistling wind doe heare,
Doe wave their tender bodies here and there;
    And though their daunce no perfect measure is,
    Yet oftentimes their musicke makes them kis.

What makes the vine about the elme to daunce,
With turnings, windings, and embracements round?
What makes the loadstone to the North advance
His subtile point, as if from thence he found
His chiefe attractive vertue to redound?
　　Kind Nature first doth cause all things to love,
　　Love makes them daunce and in just order move.

Harke how the birds doe sing, and marke then how
Jumpe with the modulation of their layes,
They lightly leape, and skip from bow to bow:
Yet doe the cranes deserve a greater prayse
Which keepe such measure in their ayrie wayes,
　　As when they all in order rankèd are,
　　They make a perfect forme triangular.

In the chiefe angle flyes the watchfull guid,
And all the followers their heads doe lay
On their foregoers backs, on eyther side;
But for the captaine hath no rest to stay,
His head forewearied with the windy way,
　　He back retires, and then the next behind,
　　As his lieuetenaunt leads them through the wind.

But why relate I every singular?
Since all the World's great fortunes and affaires
Forward and backward rapt and whirled are,
According to the musicke of the spheares:
And Chaunge herselfe her nimble feete upbeares
　　On a round slippery wheele that rowleth ay,
　　And turnes all States with her impervous sway.

Learne then to daunce, you that are Princes borne,
And lawfull lords of earthly creatures all;
Imitate them, and thereof take no scorne,

For this new art to them is naturall –
And imitate the starres cœlestiall:
  For when pale Death your vital twist shall sever,
  Your better parts must daunce, with them for ever.

Physical Universe

He woke at five and, unable
to go back to sleep,
went downstairs.

A book was lying on the table
where his son had done his homework.
He took it into the kitchen,
made coffee, poured himself a cup,
and settled down to read.

'There was a local eddy in the swirling gas
of the primordial galaxy,
and a cloud was formed, the protosun,
as wide as the present solar system.

This contracted. Some of the gas
formed a diffuse, spherical nebula.
a thin disk, that cooled and flattened.
Pulled one way by its own gravity,
the other way by the sun,
it broke, forming smaller clouds,
the protoplanets. Earth
was 2000 times as wide as it is now.'

The earth was without form, and void,
and darkness was upon the face of the deep.

*

'Then the sun began to shine,
dispelling the gases and vapors,
shrinking the planets, melting earth,

[13]

separating iron and silicate
to form the core and mantle.
Continents appeared . . .'
history, civilisation,
the discovery of America
and the settling of Green Harbor,
bringing us to Tuesday, the seventh of July.

Tuesday, the day they pick up the garbage!
He leaped into action,
took the garbage bag out of its container.
tied it with a twist of wire,
and carried it out to the tool-shed,
taking care not to let the screen-door slam,
and put it in the large garbage-can
that was three-quarters full.
He kept it in the tool-shed so the raccoons
couldn't get at it.

He carried the can out to the road,
then went back into the house
and walked around, picking up newspapers
and fliers for: 'Thompson Seedless Grapes,
California's finest sweet eating';

'Scott Bathroom Tissue';

'Legislative report from Senator Ken LaValle.'

He put all this paper in a box,
and emptied the waste baskets in the two
downstairs bathrooms,
and the basket in the study.

He carried the box out to the road,
taking care not to let the screen-door slam,
and placed the box next to the garbage.

Now let the garbage men come!

*

He went back upstairs.
Susan said, 'Did you put out the garbage?'
But her eyes were closed.
She was sleeping, yet could speak in her sleep,
ask a question, even answer one.

'Yes,' he said, and climbed into bed.
She turned around to face him,
with her eyes still closed.

He thought, perhaps she's an oracle,
speaking from the Collective Unconscious.
He said to her, 'Do you agree with Darwin
that people and monkeys have a common ancestor?
Or should we stick to the Bible?'

She said, 'Did you take out the garbage?'

'Yes,' he said, for the second time.
Then thought about it. Her answer
had something in it of the sublime.
Like a *koan* . . . the kind of irrelevance
a Zen-master says to the disciple
who is asking riddles of the universe.

He put his arm around her,
and she continued to breathe evenly
from the depths of sleep.

The dissolution of the world proovd from the mortallity of every part

And (Memmius) least you thinke I false grounds lay,
When I of fire, ayre, earth and water, say
That each of them is mortall, dayly dies
And doth againe from dissolutions rise.
First know, parts of the earth with the suns heate
Scorcht dayly, and worne out with trav'lers feete,
Exhale thick clouds of dust, which every where
Blowne with wild winds, are scatterd into ayre.
Part of the furrows wast with every showre,
And the encroaching floods their banks devoure.
   Earth for her part made by her fruitfull womb
   The generall mother, is the common tomb.
   Soe wasts she all which there have birth or food,
   Soe is herselfe diminisht and renewd.

Cascadilla Falls

I went down by Cascadilla
Falls this
evening, the
stream below the falls,
and picked up a
handsized stone
kidney-shaped, testicular, and

thought all its motions into it,
the 800 mph earth spin,
the 190-million-mile yearly
displacement around the sun,
the overriding
grand
haul

of the galaxy with the 30,000
mph of where
the sun's going:
thought all the interweaving
motions
into myself: dropped

the stone to dead rest:
the stream from other motions
broke
rushing over it:
shelterless,
I turned

to the sky and stood still:
oh
I do
not know where I am going
that I can live my life
by this single creek.

The Black Stars

Let no one sing again of love or war.

The order from which the cosmos took its name has been
    dissolved;
The heavenly legions are a tangle of monsters,
The universe – blind, violent and strange – assails us.
The sky is strewn with horrible dead suns,
Dense sediments of mangled atoms.
Only desperate heaviness emanates from them,
Not energy, not messages, not particles, not light.
Light itself falls back down, broken by its own weight,
And all of us human seed, we live and die for nothing,
The skies perpetually revolve in vain.

Translated by Ruth Feldman and Brian Swann

The Doctor of Starlight

'Show me the place,' he said.
I removed my shirt and pointed
to a tiny star above my heart.
He leaned and listened. I could feel
his breath falling lightly, flattening
the hairs on my chest. He turned
me around, and his hands gently
plied my shoulder blades and then rose
to knead the twin columns forming
my neck. 'You are an athlete?'
'No,' I said, 'I'm a working man.'
'And you make?' he said. 'I make
the glare for lightbulbs.' 'Yes,
where would we be without them?'
'In the dark.' I heard the starched
dress of the nurse behind me,
and then together they helped me
lie face up on his table, where blind
and helpless I thought of all
the men and women who had surrendered
and how little good it had done them.
The nurse took my right wrist
in both of her strong hands, and I
saw the doctor lean toward me,
a tiny chrome knife glinting in
one hand and tweezers in the other.
I could feel nothing, and then he said
proudly, 'I have it!' and held up
the perfect little blue star, no

longer me and now bloodless. 'And do
you know what we have under it?'
'No,' I said. 'Another perfect star.'
I closed my eyes, but the lights
still swam before me in a sea
of golden fire. 'What does it mean?'
'Mean?' he said, dabbing the place
with something cool and liquid,
and all the lights were blinking on
and off, or perhaps my eyes were
opening and closing. 'Mean?' he said,
'It could mean this is who you are.'

PETER REDGROVE

In the Lab with the Lady Doctor

The Old Woman resembles a fairy-tale princess
Who has stayed too long in her tower unrescued,
She precedes me among the benches, she puts
Her protective goggles on, and in this mood
Resembles that gnome who captured me; I look closer:
It is that gnome. She comes in again
With a flock of young men in white flapping coats
To whom she is goosegirl. I insist that the chemicals
On this side of the bench are strictly mine, and this includes
The bottle of gold salts, and the retort distilling
An infusion of bull-semen. There will be a fight, it's plain,
One of the young Privatdocents has his white coat off
    already
Underneath which he is naked, and in mock compliment I
    reach out
And shake him firmly by the wedding-muscle, upon which
He hits me all over maybe sixty times
In five seconds with karate blows, one of which
Catches me near my Person but safely thuds
On pubic bone, and I declare 'This assault should not
Have helped your case, but nevertheless this does not mean
That certain experiments cannot be performed in joint
    names . . .'
At my resolve, a spattering of applause, and the Old Girl
Crosses over from her young squires in dazzling plumage
And asks to see the bruises, so I strip off my shirt.
The marks of striking hands patter across my chest
And already the dark bruises are rainbowing like pieces
Of peacock tail. The young chap who inflicted them

Stands by, sniffing my retort's nozzle; with a shyly winning
    smile
'Will you give me a drink of this?' he asks. I feel like a fruit
Which has been bruised in order to ferment
Some delicious rare liquor; I say so; they applaud again.

Ode upon Doctor Harvey

Coy Nature, (which remain'd, thô aged grown,
A beauteous Virgin still, injoy'd by none,
  Nor seen unveil'd by any one,)
When *Harvey's* violent passion she did see,
Began to tremble and to flee,
Took Sanctuary, like *Daphne*, in a Tree:
There *Daphne's* Lover stopt, and thought it much
  The very Leaves of her to touch:
But *Harvey*, our *Apollo*, stopt not so,
Into the Bark and Root he after her did go:
  No smallest Fibres of a Plant,
For which the Eye-beams point doth sharpness want,
  His passage after her withstood;
What should she do? through all the moving Wood
Of Lives endow'd with sense she took her flight,
Harvey persues, and keeps her still in sight.
But as the Deer, long hunted, takes a Flood,
She leap'd at last into the Winding-streams of Blood;
Of Mans *Meander* all the Purple reaches made,
  Till at the Heart she stay'd,
  Where turning Head, and at a Bay,
Thus by well-purged Ears she was o're-heard to say.

Here sure shall I be safe (said she,)
None will be able sure to see
  This my Retreat, but only He
  Who made both it and me.
The heart of Man, what Art can e're reveal?
  A Wall impervious between
  Divides the very Parts within,

[24]

And doth the very Heart of Man ev'n from itself conceal.
      She spoke, but e're she was aware,
      Harvey was with her there,
And held this slippery *Proteus* in a chain,
Till all her mighty Mysteries she descry'd,
Which from his Wit th' attempt before to hide
Was the first Thing that Nature did in vain.

      He the young Practice of New Life did see,
      Whil'st, to conceal it's toilsome poverty,
It for a Living wrought, both hard, and privately.
      Before the Liver understood
      The noble Scarlet Dye of Blood,
      Before one drop was by it made,
Or brought into it to set up the Trade;
Before the untaught Heart began to beat
The tuneful March to vital heat,
From all the Souls that living Buildings rear,
Whether imploy'd for Earth, or Sea, or Air,
Whether it in the Womb or Egg be wrought,
A strict account to him is hourly brought,
      How the great Fabrick does proceed,
What Time, and what Materials it does need.
He so exactly does the Work survey,
As if he hir'd the Workers by the day.

Thus *Harvey* sought for Truth in Truth's own Book,
      The Creatures, which by God himself was writ;
      And wisely thought 'twas fit,
Not to read Comments only upon it,
But on th' Original itself to look.
Methinks in Arts great Circle others stand
      Lock'd up together hand in hand,
      Every one leads as he is led,

The same bare Path they tread.
A Dance like Fairies, a Fantastick round,
But neither change their Motion, nor their Ground.
Had *Harvey* to this Road confin'd his Wit,
His noble Circle of the Blood had been untroden yet:
Great Doctor, th' art of Curing's cur'd by thee,
    We now thy Patient Physick see
From all inveterate Diseases free,
    Purg'd of old Errors by thy Care,
New Dieted, put forth to clearer Air,
        It now will strong and healthful prove,
Itself before Lethargick lay, and could not move.

These useful Secrets to his Pen we owe,
And thousands more 'twas ready to bestow;
Of which a barbarous War's unlearned Rage
        Has robb'd the ruin'd age;
Oh cruel loss! as if the Golden Fleece,
        With so much cost and labour wrought,
And from afar by a great Heroe brought,
        Had sunk even in the Ports of *Greece*.
Oh cursed War! who can forgive thee this?
        Houses and Towns may rise again,
        And ten times easier 'tis
To rebuild *Pauls*, than any work of his.
The mighty Task none but himself can do,
    Nay, scarce himself too now,
For tho' his Wit the force of Age withstand,
His body Alas! and Time it must command.
And Nature now, so long by him surpast,
Will sure have her revenge on him at last.

from The Art of Preserving Health

The blood, the fountain whence the spirits flow,
The generous stream that waters every part,
And motion, vigour, and warm life conveys
To every particle that moves or lives;
This vital fluid, through unnumbered tubes
Poured by the heart, and to the heart again
Refunded; scourged for ever round and round;
Enraged with heat and toil, at last forgets
Its balmy nature; virulent and thin
It grows; and now, but that a thousand gates
Are open to its flight, it would destroy
The parts it cherished and repaired before.
Besides, the flexible and tender tubes
Melt in the mildest, most nectareous tide
That ripening Nature rolls; as in the stream
Its crumbling banks; but what the vital force
Of plastic fluids hourly batters down,
That very force, those plastic particles
Rebuild: so mutable the state of man.
For this the watchful appetite was given,
Daily with fresh materials to repair
This unavoidable expense of life,
This necessary waste of flesh and blood.
Hence the concoctive powers, with various art,
Subdue the cruder aliments to chyle;
The chyle to blood; the foamy purple tide
To liquors, which through finer arteries

To different parts their winding course pursue;
To try new changes, and new forms put on,
Or for the public, or some private use.

Calcium

Because I love the very bones of you,
and you are somehow rooted in my bone,
I'll tell you of the seven years

by which the skeleton renews itself,
so that we have the chance to be
a person, now and then, who's

something other than ourselves;
and how the body, if deficient,
will bleed the calcium it needs –

for heart, for liver, spleen –
from bone, which incidentally,
I might add, is not the thorough

structure that you might
suppose, but living tissue which
the doctors say a woman of my age

should nurture mindfully with fruit,
weightbearing exercise, and supplements
to halt the dangers of a fracture when I'm old;

and because I love you I will also tell
how stripped of skin the papery bone
is worthy of inscription, could hold

a detailed record of a navy or a store of grain,
and how, if it's preserved
according to the pharaohs,

wrapped in bandages of coca leaf, tobacco,
it will survive long after all our books,
and even words are weightless;

and perhaps because the heaviness of your head,
the way I love the slow, sweet sense of you,
the easiness by which you're stilled,

how the fleshy structures that your skeleton,
your skull maintain, are easily interrogated,
it reminds me how our hands,

clasped for a moment, now, amount
to everything I have; how even your smile
as it breaks me up, has the quality of ice,

the long lines of loneliness
like a lifetime ploughed across a palm,
the permanence of snow.

from The Spleen

In vain to chase thee, every Art we try;
In vain all Remedies apply;
In vain the *Indian* leaf infuse,
Or the pearch'd Eastern Berry bruise;
Some pass in vain those bounds, and nobler Liquors use.
Now Harmony in vain we bring,
Inspire the Flute, and touch the String;
From Harmony no help is had:
Musick but sooths thee, if too sweetly sad;
And if too light, but turns thee gladly mad.
Not skilful *Lower* thy Source cou'd find,
Or through the well-dissected Body trace
The secret and mysterious ways,
By which thou dost destroy and prey upon the Mind;
Tho' in the Search, too deep for Humane Thought,
With unsuccessful Toil he wrought,
'Till in pursuit of thee himself was by thee caught;
Retain'd thy Prisoner, thy acknowledg'd Slave,
And sunk beneath thy Weight to a lamented Grave.

The Urine Specimen

In the clinic, a sun-bleached shell of stone
on the shore of the city, you enter
the last small chamber, a little closet
chastened with pearl, cool, white, and glistening,
and over the chilly well of the toilet
you trickle your precious sum in a cup.
It's as simple as that. But the heat
of this gold your body's melted and poured out
into a form begins to enthrall you,
warming your hand with your flesh's fevers
in a terrible way. It's like holding
an organ – spleen or fatty pancreas,
a lobe from your foamy brain still steaming
with worry. You know that just outside
a nurse is waiting to cool it into a gel
and slice it onto a microscope slide
for the doctor, who in it will read your future,
wringing his hands. You lift the chalice and toast
the long life of your friend there in the mirror,
who wanly smiles, but does not drink to you.

LAVINIA GREENLAW

The Man Whose Smile Made Medical History

On dead afternoons my brother would borrow
rubber gloves and wellington boots
to chance the electrics of the ancient projector.

We would interrupt fifty-year-old summers where
a woman I now know in nappies and a walking frame
played leapfrog on a beach in West Wales

with a man whose smile made medical history.
The First World War revealed the infinite
possibilities of the human form,

so when in '16 he was sent back from France
without his top lip, the army doctors
decided to try and grow him a new one.

They selected the stomach as the ideal place
from which to tease a flap of skin
into a handle that could be stretched

and sewn to what was left of his mouth.
This additional feature was surgically removed
once it had fed the regeneration

of a thankfully familiar shape.
All I can find in my grandfather's face
to record the birth of plastic surgery

is the tight shyness he pulls into a grin,
unaware that scientific progress
which had saved his reflection could do nothing

to save his life. A doctor, aged thirty-four,
he died of viral pneumonia,
having recently heard of antibiotics.

The Spirit is too Blunt an Instrument

The spirit is too blunt an instrument
to have made this baby.
Nothing so unskilful as human passions
could have managed the intricate
exacting particulars: the tiny
blind bones with their manipulating tendons,
the knee and the knucklebones, the resilient
fine meshings of ganglia and vertebrae
in the chain of the difficult spine.

Observe the distinct eyelashes and sharp crescent
fingernails, the shell-like complexity
of the ear with its firm involutions
concentric in miniature to the minute
ossicles. Imagine the
infinitesimal capillaries, the flawless connections
of the lungs, the invisible neural filaments
through which the completed body
already answers to the brain.

Then name any passion or sentiment
possessed of the simplest accuracy.
No. No desire or affection could have done
with practice what habit
has done perfectly, indifferently,
through the body's ignorant precision.
It is left to the vagaries of the mind to invent
love and despair and anxiety
and their pain.

from Nosce Teipsum
in what manner the soule is united to the body

But how shall we this *union* well expresse?
   Nought ties the *soule*; her subtiltie is such
   She moves the bodie, which she doth possesse,
   Yet no part toucheth, but by *Vertue's* touch.

Then dwels shee not therein as in a tent,
   Nor as a pilot in his ship doth sit;
   Nor as the spider in his web is pent;
   Nor as the waxe retaines the print in it;

Nor as a vessell water doth containe;
   Nor as one liquor in another shed;
   Nor as the heat doth in the fire remaine;
   Nor as a voice throughout the ayre is spread:

But as the faire and cheerfull *Morning light*,
   Doth here and there her silver beames impart,
   And in an instant doth herselfe unite
   To the transparent ayre, in all, and part:

Still resting whole, when blowes the ayre divide;
   Abiding pure, when th'ayre is most corrupted;
   Throughout the ayre, her beams dispersing wide,
   And when the ayre is tost, not interrupted:

So doth the piercing *Soule* the body fill,
   Being all in all, and all in part diffus'd;
   Indivisible, incorruptible still,
   Not forc't, encountred, troubled or confus'd.

And as the *sunne* above, the light doth bring,
   Though we behold it in the ayre below;
   So from th' Eternall Light the *Soule* doth spring,
   Though in the body she her powers doe show.

from Of the Progress of the Soul
Her ignorance in this life

Poor soul, in this thy flesh what dost thou know?
Thou know'st thyself so little, as thou know'st not,
How thou didst die, nor how thou wast begot.
Thou neither know'st, how thou at first cam'st in,
Nor how thou took'st the poison of man's sin.
Nor dost thou, (though thou know'st, that thou art so)
By what way thou art made immortal, know.
Thou art too narrow, wretch, to comprehend
Even thyself; yea though thou wouldst but bend
To know thy body. Have not all souls thought
For many ages, that our body is wrought
Of air, and fire, and other elements?
And now they think of new ingredients,
And one soul thinks one, and another way
Another thinks, and 'tis an even lay.
Know'st thou but how the stone doth enter in
The bladder's cave, and never break the skin?
Know'st thou how blood, which to the heart doth flow,
Doth from one ventricle to th' other go?
And for the putrid stuff, which thou dost spit,
Know'st thou how thy lungs have attracted it?
There are no passages, so that there is
(For aught thou know'st) piercing of substances.
And of those many opinions which men raise
Of nails and hairs, dost thou know which to praise?
What hope have we to know our selves, when we
Know not the least things, which for our use be? [. . .]

Why grass is green, or why our blood is red,
Are mysteries which none have reached unto.
In this low form, poor soul, what wilt thou do?
When wilt thou shake off this pedantery,
Of being taught by sense, and fantasy?
Thou look'st through spectacles; small things seem great
Below; but up unto the watch-tower get,
And see all things despoiled of fallacies:
Thou shalt not peep through lattices of eyes,
Nor hear through labyrinths of ears, nor learn
By circuit, or collections to discern.

DON PATERSON

The Lover
after Propertius

Poor mortals, with your horoscopes and blood-tests –
what hope is there for you? Even if the plane
lands you safely, why should you not return
to your home in flames or ruins, your wife absconded,
the children blind and dying in their cots?
Even sitting quiet in a locked room
the perils are infinite and unforeseeable.
Only the lover walks upon the earth
careless of what the fates prepare for him:

so you step out at the lights, almost as if
you half-know that today you are the special one.
The woman in the windshield lifting away
her frozen cry, a white mask on a stick,
reveals herself as grey-eyed Atropos;
the sun leaves like a rocket; the sky goes out;
the road floods and widens; on the distant kerb
the lost souls groan and mew like sad trombones;
the ambulance glides up with its black sail –

when somewhere in the other world, she fills
your name full of her breath again, and at once
you float to your feet: the dark rose on your shirt
folds itself away, and you slip back
into the crowd, who, being merely human,
must remember nothing of this incident.
Just one flea-ridden dog chained to the railings,
who might be Cerberus, or patient Argos,
looks on, knowing the great law you have flouted.

Entropy

Your coffee grows cold on the kitchen table,
which means the universe is dying.
Your dress on the carpet is just a dress,
it has lost all sense of you now.
I open the window, the sky is dark
and the house is also cooling, the garden,
the summer lawn, all of it finding an equilibrium.
I watch an ice-cube melt in my wine,
the heat of the Chardonnay passing into the ice.
It means the universe is dying: the second law
of thermodynamics. Entropy rising.
Only the fridge struggles to turn things round
but even here there's a hidden loss.
It hums in the corner, the only sound
on a quiet night. Outside, in the vast sky
stars are cooling. I think of the sun
consuming its fuel, the afternoon that is past,
and your dress that only this morning
was warm to my touch.

More Machines

The clock of love? A smallish, round affair
That fits in the palm. A handy prop
Like any of these: compare
The pebble, the pearl, and the water drop.
They're all well made. But only one will prove
A fitting timepiece for our love.

To the pebble, the sun is a meteor,
The days a strobe, the years are swift.
Its machinery moves imperceptibly
Like the stars and continental drift.
But it's not for timing human love – it never *stops*.
Let us consider then the water drop

As it falls from the spigot during a summer storm
A distance of three feet. What does it see?
The lightning etched forever on the hot slate sky,
The birds fixed in an eternal V . . .
It falls so fast it knows no growth or changes.
A quick dog-fuck is all it measures

And it serves the beast as the stone serves God.
But our love doesn't hold with natural law.
Accept this small glass planet then, a shard
Grown smooth inside an oyster's craw.
Like us, it learns to opalesce
In darkness, in cold depths, in timelessness.

ALBERT GOLDBARTH

Arguing Bartusiak

*Space-time simply doesn't exist where loop lines are absent, any more than
a blanket exists between the weave of its threads.*

Marcia Bartusiak, in a science article

The idea is, the marriage still exists
when they're at different coasts for the summer:
her job, his ailing parents. Some weeks
even fax- and phone-chat thins
to a nebular frizzle the instruments barely acknowledge.
Even so, she knows she knows she's married and
she *thinks* she knows he knows it too.
She imagines him now, he's walking through the garden
of the house in Palo Verde, in the dawnlight there
that always looks so unsoiled, so
historically uninhabited-through; and in the face
of the coffee and its seemingly prescient tentacles of steam,
he sees the day ahead, a day of salt baths
and colostomy bags, of people one loves monolithically
going grain by grain to something
a son can only sift through, shaking his head.
In a way, although the thought is shameful, she
envies him this: the lug and grunt of working
human necessities – enormous grand pianos
of human distress and their human solutions – across
the convolute rooms of a day. For her, the world is all
    abstraction
and the iffiness of quarkish nonevents, for her
it's less than air, since air of course is elements
imperturbable and ponderous by her standards
– she's a theoretician of quantum gravity models, and
she uses a machine the size of a shopping mall

[43]

to track the ghostly geysering of particles that exist
so far in hypothesis only. It's *beautiful*,
it's *consummatory*, labor; but some mornings
when she walks along the squabble of Atlantic water
and Jersey shore, she feels the need
to hug herself, to keep herself
from suddenly evaporating into the between-states
of her studies. Or to have *somebody*
hug her. That night, at Kelly's Reef,
as a patchwork jazz quartet is into its last set,
Mr Silk-'n-Sip – a friend of a friend
of a friend, who's magically latched on to their party –
makes the thousand invisible signs of availability.
His hands are shapely and capable. His stories
encompass plasma physics, Van Gogh connoisseurship,
Tantric sex techniques. She's crazy
to say no, but she says no. It's 4 a.m.
and in the rumple of her by-the-month
efficiency apartment, in her sleeplessness,
she idly works the gold ring off her finger, lets the light
trace its solidity, then puffs a single
breath through its empty center. It's late,
she's sleepy at last, she
wraps herself in her blanket, and
if some of it, *somewhere* in it, isn't blanket,
she wraps herself in that too.

Translation from an Unwritten Poem

Though we are separated by so great a distance, the world is yet small enough for us to have the same land-marks.

Let us on a certain day at the same time arrange to gaze on the sun, the apex of a triangle, the longer sides of which link us, though the shorter separates.

But the sun's kindly light may not be endured; let us rather both gaze on the kindly and knowledgeable moon, the traditional friend of lovers.

And yet the moon is not reliable; it is of no use, without artificial calendars. Let us therefore make as our final choice, the North Star, the firmest thing in our universe.

And let us pray that there be a cloudless sky on that momentous night, that we may, whilst yet alive, enjoy one of the advantages of eternity.

A Foreplay

I'll entertain questions before the stellar estrus
   commences: if you want.
      But since it's you I depend on
      to change the lines to living

ground and figure, I'd rather have you
find the answers on your own. Remember how

   music was aroused in the old technology?
The stylus vibrated, shaking a crystal in its head,
   and the groove culled this trembling.
The stylus made electrons fly
   from the atom, climb a wire through
the crystal to the gate. There

   the slight current was amplified,
bridling the large –

   and vinyl gave
rise to sonatas, rise to bop.

   This gives the odd god
and hound dog, dolphin and electron,
   the novation and the moment
of change. Since the truly new
looks truly wrong at first,

   it gives the sublime and grotesque,
hoping you'll receive them kindly,
hoping for the best – newness
   being not so much a truth

as it is emotion.
Can you feel for the dark

    matter, background
lines of lace or brides? Will you
    receive the hybridized and recombined,
the downsized and the amplified?

The greenery and systemic herbicide:
    the laurel wreath.

    As estrogenic effects collect –
in heat and blur and curve – will you receive
    the minus and the plus,
the – not to mention, but I must –

    then some inbetween?

The Ex-queen among the Astronomers

They serve revolving saucer eyes,
dishes of stars; they wait upon
huge lenses hung aloft to frame
the slow procession of the skies.

They calculate, adjust, record,
watch transits, measure distances.
They carry pocket telescopes
to spy through when they walk abroad.

Spectra possess their eyes; they face
upwards, alert for meteorites,
cherishing little glassy worlds:
receptacles for outer space.

But she, exile, expelled, ex-queen,
swishes among the men of science
waiting for cloudy skies, for nights
when constellations can't be seen.

She wears the rings he let her keep;
she walks as she was taught to walk
for his approval, years ago.
His bitter features taunt her sleep.

And so when these have laid aside
their telescopes, when lids are closed
between machine and sky, she seeks
terrestrial bodies to bestride.

She plucks this one or that among
the astronomers, and is become

his canopy, his occultation;
she sucks at earlobe, penis, tongue

mouthing the tubes of flesh; her hair
crackles, her eyes are comet-sparks.
She brings the distant briefly close
above his dreamy abstract stare.

The Golden Wall

Don't ask Uncle Pat why the night sky is dark –
in hot weather
taking his mattress out on the grass
inside his dog-proof fence to sleep.
When Pat lifts his face up to the night –
propped on a pillow
of kapok stuffed in mattress ticking –
he'd fix you with sheep drench if you told him
that his line of sight
should intersect at every point
with a near or distant star
glimmering in the transparency of space
so the whole sky
should be ablaze from end to end
like 'a golden wall'.
Pat's golden wall was his orange tree.
Like Uncle Pat it had never borne fruit
until I dumped five tons of chicken manure
on its roots.
His line of sight
from the cane lounge where he sprawled
intersected at every point with oranges
twenty feet up in the sky,
a Utopia of fruit
which the district came to visit and eat,
oranges with no ending
like the return veranda
around the four sides of his house

where nephews and nieces ran forever
and their children after them.

Pat forgot his promise to pay for the manure
and the oranges didn't come back.
But he didn't miss them,
so don't ask Pat why the night sky is dark.

Olbers' riddle has hung around
for centuries.
You can't explain it by absorption.
Gas and dust heat up and glow.
Nor by absences or voids.
Every square inch has its galaxies.

Ask the cells inside your head
the same riddle,
why don't they all blaze at once
a golden wall of noise,
each neuron singing its own note
deafening your mind with light.
Political and religious visionaries
promise us this,
every cell singing in unison,
a mass of indistinguishable stars.

But something in the universe denies
the golden wall,
some structure which became Uncle Pat
calling to his nephews from his cane lounge,
'Now don't trample them tomahawk plants!'
(meaning hollyhock plants).

Pat prefers his own company on hot nights
leaving Auntie Bridge inside

with pictures of saints on the bedroom wall.
He takes his bedding
and lies in a darkness
where each star can broadcast as a soloist.

The universe
is a composition of unique bodies
on display,
and the night sky of the mind
allows a single file of thoughts
to light up as a sentence.

Ontario

I spent last night in the nursery of a house in Pennsylvania. When I put out the light I made my way, barefoot, through the aftermath of Brandywine Creek. The constellations of the northern hemisphere were picked out in luminous paint on the ceiling. I lay under a comforting, phosphorescent Plough, thinking about where the Plough stopped being the Plough and became the Big Dipper. About the astronomer I met in Philadelphia who had found a star with a radio telescope. The star is now named after her, whatever her name happens to be. As all these stars grew dim, it seemed like a good time to rerun my own dream-visions. They had flashed up just as I got into bed on three successive nights in 1972. The first was a close-up of a face, Cox's face, falling. I heard next morning how he had come home drunk and taken a nose-dive down the stairs. Next, my uncle Pat's face, falling in slo-mo like the first, but bloody. It turned out he had slipped off a ladder on a building-site. His forehead needed seven stitches. Lastly, a freeze-frame trickle of water or glycerine on a sheet of smoked glass or perspex. I see it in shaving-mirrors. Dry Martinis. Women's tears. On windshields. As planes take off or land. I remembered how I was meant to fly to Toronto this morning, to visit my younger brother. He used to be a research assistant at the University of Guelph, where he wrote a thesis on nitrogen-fixing in soya beans, or symbiosis, or some such mystery. He now works for the Corn Producers' Association of Ontario. On my last trip we went to a disco in the Park Plaza, where I helped a girl in a bin-liner dress to find her contact-lens.

– Did you know that Spinoza was a lens-grinder?

– Are you for real?

Joe was somewhere in the background, sniggering, flicking cosmic dandruff from his shoulders.

– A lens, I went on, is really a lentil. A pulse.

Her back was an imponderable, green furrow in the ultraviolet strobe.

– Did *you* know that Yonge Street's the longest street in the world?

– I can't say that I did.

– Well, it starts a thousand miles to the north, and it ends right here.

SAMUEL BUTLER

from The Elephant in the Moon

A learned society of late,
The glory of a foreign state,
Agreed, upon a summer's night,
To search the Moon by her own light;
To make an inventory of all
Her real estate, and personal;
And make an accurate survey
Of all her lands, and how they lay,
As true as that of Ireland, where
The sly surveyors stole a shire:
T' observe her country, how 'twas planted,
With what sh' abounded most, or wanted;
And make the proper'st observations
For settling of new plantations,
If the society should incline
T' attempt so glorious a design.

This was the purpose of their meeting,
For which they chose a time as fitting;
When at the full her radiant light
And influence too were at their height.
And now the lofty tube, the scale
With which they heaven itself assail,
Was mounted full against the Moon;
And all stood ready to fall on,
Impatient who should have the honour
To plant an ensign first upon her.
When one, who for his deep belief
Was virtuoso then in chief,
Approved the most profound, and wise,

To solve impossibilities,
Advancing gravely, to apply
To th' optic glass his judging eye,
Cried, 'Strange!' – then reinforced his sight
Against the Moon with all his might,
And bent his penetrating brow,
As if he meant to gaze her through;
When all the rest began t' admire,
And, like a train, from him took fire,
Surprised with wonder, beforehand,
At what they did not understand,
Cried out, impatient to know what
The matter was they wondered at.

    Quoth he, 'Th' inhabitants o' th' Moon,
Who, when the Sun shines hot at noon,
Do live in cellars underground,
Of eight miles deep, and eighty round,
In which at once they fortify
Against the sun and th' enemy,
Which they count towns and cities there,
Because their people's civiller
Than those rude peasants, that are found
To live upon the upper ground,
Called Privolvans, with whom they are
Perpetually in open war;
And now both armies, highly enraged,
Are in a bloody fight engaged,
And many fall on both sides slain,
As by the glass 'tis clear, and plain.
Look quickly then, that every one
May see the fight before 'tis done.'

    With that a great philosopher,
Admired, and famous far and near,

As one of singular invention,
But universal comprehension,
Applied one eye, and half a nose
Unto the optic engine close.

Quoth he, 'A stranger sight appears
Than e'er was seen in all the spheres,
A wonder more unparalleled,
Than ever mortal tube beheld;
An elephant from one of those
Two mighty armies is broke loose,
And with the horror of the fight
Appears amazed, and in a fright;
Look quickly, lest the sight of us
Should cause the startled beast t' imboss.
It is a large one, far more great
Than e'er was bred in Afric yet;
From which we boldly may infer,
The Moon is much the fruitfuller.

'Most excellent and virtuous friends,
This great discovery makes amends
For all our unsuccessful pains,
And lost expense of time and brains.
For, by this sole phenomenon,
We 'ave gotten ground upon the Moon;
And gained a pass, to hold dispute
With all the planets that stand out;
To carry this most virtuous war
Home to the door of every star,
And plant th' artillery of our tubes
Against their proudest magnitudes . . .'

This said, they all with one consent,
Agreed to draw up th' instrument,
And, for the general satisfaction,
To print it in the next 'Transaction.'
    But, whilst the chiefs were drawing up
This strange memoir o' th' telescope,
One, peeping in the tube by chance,
Beheld the elephant advance.
And, from the west side of the Moon
To th' east was in a moment gone.
This being related, gave a stop
To what the rest were drawing up;
And every man, amazed anew
How it could possibly be true,
That any beast should run a race
So monstrous, in so short a space,
Resolved, howe'er, to make it good,
At least, as possible as he could;
And rather his own eyes condemn,
Than question what he 'ad seen with them . . .

But, while they were diverted all
With wording the memorial,
The footboys, for diversion too,
As having nothing else to do,
Seeing the telescope at leisure,
Turned virtuosos for their pleasure;
Began to gaze upon the Moon,
As those they waited on, had done,
With monkeys' ingenuity,
That love to practise what they see;
When one, whose turn it was to peep,
Saw something in the engine creep;

And, viewing well, discovered more
Than all the learned had done before.
Quoth he, 'A little thing is slunk
Into the long star-gazing trunk;
And now is gotten down so nigh,
I have him just against mine eye.'
    This being overheard by one,
Who was not so far overgrown
In any virtuous speculation,
To judge with mere imagination,
Immediately he made a guess
At solving all appearances,
A way far more significant,
Than all their hints of th' elephant,
And found, upon a second view,
His own hypothesis most true;
For he had scarce applied his eye
To th' engine, but immediately
He found a mouse was gotten in
The hollow tube, and, shut between
The two glass windows in restraint
Was swelled into an elephant;
And proved the virtuous occasion
Of all this learnèd dissertation;
And, as a mountain heretofore
Was great with child, they say, and bore
A silly mouse; this mouse, as strange,
Brought forth a mountain, in exchange.

Brief Reflection on Accuracy

Fish
    always accurately know where to move and when,
    and likewise
    birds have an accurate built-in time sense
    and orientation.

Humanity, however,
    lacking such instincts resorts to scientific
    research. Its nature is illustrated by the following
    occurrence.

A certain soldier
    had to fire a cannon at six o'clock sharp every evening.
    Being a soldier he did so. When his accuracy was
    investigated he explained:

I go by
    the absolutely accurate chronometer in the window
    of the clockmaker down in the city. Every day at seventeen
    forty-five I set my watch by it and
    climb the hill where my cannon stands ready.
    At seventeen fifty-nine precisely I step up to the cannon
    and at eighteen hours sharp I fire.

And it was clear
    that this method of firing was absolutely accurate.
    All that was left was to check that chronometer. So
    the clockmaker down in the city was questioned about
    his instrument's accuracy.

Oh, said the clockmaker,
   this is one of the most accurate instruments ever. Just
      imagine,
   for many years now a cannon has been fired at six o'clock
      sharp.
   And every day I look at this chronometer
   and always it shows exactly six.

So much for accuracy.
   And fish move in the water, and from the skies
   comes a rushing of wings while

Chronometers tick and cannon boom.

Translated by Ewald Osers

Four Quartz Crystal Clocks

There are four vibrators, the world's exactest clocks;
    and these quartz time-pieces that tell
time intervals to other clocks,
    these worksless clocks work well;
independently the same, kept in
    the 41° Bell
        Laboratory time

vault. Checked by a comparator with Arlington,
    they punctualize the 'radio,
cinema,' and 'presse,' – a group the
    Giraudoux truth-bureau
of hoped-for accuracy has termed
    'instruments of truth'. We know –
        as Jean Giraudoux says

certain Arabs have not heard – that Napoleon
    is dead; that a quartz prism when
the temperature changes, feels
    the change and that the then
electrified alternate edges
    oppositely charged, threaten
        careful timing; so that

this water-clear crystal as the Greeks used to say,
    this 'clear ice' must be kept at the
same coolness. Repetition, with
    the scientist, should be
synonymous with accuracy.
    The lemur-student can see
        that an aye-aye is not

an angwan-tibo, potto, or loris. The seaside burden should not embarrass
the bell-boy with the buoy-ball
   endeavouring to pass
hotel patronesses; nor could a
   practised ear confuse the glass
      eyes for taxidermists

with eye-glasses from the optometrist. And as
   MEridian-7 one-two
one-two gives, each fifteenth second
   in the same voice, the new
data – 'The time will be' so and so –
   you realize that 'when you
      hear the signal', you'll be

hearing Jupiter or jour pater, the day god –
   the salvaged son of Father Time –
telling the cannibal Chronos
   (eater of his proxime
newborn progeny) that punctuality
   is not a crime.

Cicadas

You know those windless summer evenings, swollen to stasis
by too-substantial melodies, rich as a
running-down record, ground round
to full quiet. Even the leaves
have thick tongues.

And if the first crickets quicken then,
other inhabitants, at window or door
or rising from table, feel in the lungs
a slim false-freshness, by this
trick of the ear.

Chanters of miracles took for a simple sign
the Latin cicada, because of his long waiting
and sweet change in daylight, and his singing
all his life, pinched on the ash leaf,
heedless of ants.

Others made morals; all were puzzled and joyed
by this gratuitous song. Such a plain thing
morals could not surround, nor listening:
not 'chirr' nor 'cri-cri.' There is no straight
way of approaching it.

This thin uncomprehended song it is
springs healing questions into binding air.
Fabre, by firing all the municipal cannon
under a piping tree, found out
cicadas cannot hear.

from The House of Fame

'Soun ys noght but eyr ybroken,
And every speche that ys spoken,
Lowd or pryvee, foul or fair,
In his substaunce ys but air;
For as flaumbe ys but lyghted smoke,
Ryght soo soun ys air ybroke.
But this may be in many wyse,
Of which I wil the twoo devyse,
As soun that cometh of pipe or harpe.
For whan a pipe is blowen sharpe,
The air ys twyst with violence
And rent; loo, thys ys my sentence;
Eke, whan men harpe-strynges smyte,
Whether hyt be moche or lyte,
Loo, with the strok the ayr tobreketh;
And ryght so breketh it when men speketh.
Thus wost thou wel what thing is speche.
    'Now hennesforth y wol the teche
How every speche, or noyse, or soun,
Thurgh hys multiplicacioun,
Thogh hyt were piped of a mous,
Mot nede come to Fames Hous.
I preve hyt thus – take hede now –
Be experience; for yf that thow
Throwe on water now a stoon,
Wel wost thou, hyt wol make anoon
A litel roundell as a sercle,
Paraunter brod as a covercle;
And ryght anoon thow shalt see wel,

[65]

That whel wol cause another whel,
And that the thridde, and so forth, brother,
Every sercle causynge other
Wydder than hymselve was;
And thus fro roundel to compas,
Ech aboute other goynge
Causeth of othres sterynge
And multiplyinge ever moo,
Til that hyt be so fer ygoo,
That hyt at bothe brynkes bee.
Although thou mowe hyt not ysee
Above, hyt gooth yet always under,
Although thou thenke hyt a gret wonder.
And whoso seyth of trouthe I varye,
Bid hym proven the contrarye.
And ryght thus every word, ywys,
That lowd or pryvee spoken ys,
Moveth first an ayr aboute,
And of thys movynge, out of doute,
Another ayr anoon ys meved,
As I have of the watir preved,
That every cercle causeth other.
Ryght so of ayr, my leve brother;
Everych ayr another stereth
More and more, and speche up bereth,
Or voys, or noyse, or word, or soun,
Ay through multiplicacioun,
Til hyt be atte Hous of Fame, –
Take yt in ernest or in game.

    'Now have I told, yf thou have mynde,
How speche or soun, of pure kynde,
Enclyned ys upward to meve;
This, mayst thou fele, wel I preve.

And that same place, ywys,
That every thyng enclyned to ys,
Hath his kyndelyche stede:
That sheweth hyt, withouten drede,
That kyndely the mansioun
Of every speche, of every soun,
Be hyt eyther foul or fair,
Hath hys kynde place in ayr.
And syn that every thyng that is
Out of hys kynde place, ywys,
Moveth thidder for to goo,
Yif hyt aweye be therfroo,
As I have before preved the,
Hyt seweth, every soun, parde,
Moveth kyndely to pace
Al up into his kyndely place.
And this place of which I telle,
Ther as Fame lyst to duelle,
Ys set amyddys of these three,
Heven, erthe, and eke the see,
As most conservatyf the soun.
Than ys this the conclusyoun,
That every speche of every man,
As y the telle first began,
Moveth up on high to pace
Kyndely to Fames place.

pryvee, softly; *devyse*; explain; *sentence*, meaning; *Eke*, also; *lyte*, gently;
hennesforth, henceforth; *y*, I; *Paraunter*, perhaps; *covercle*, pot-lid; *whel*, wheel;
Wydder, wider; *ygoo*, gone; *mowe*, might; *ywys*, indeed; *leve*, dear; *syn*, since;
therfroo, from there; *seweth*, follows; *amyddys*, amidst; *conservatyf*, preserving
of.

'Split the Lark'

Split the Lark – and you'll find the Music –
Bulb after Bulb, in Silver rolled –
Scantily dealt to the Summer Morning
Saved for your Ear when Lutes be old.

Loose the Flood – you shall find it patent –
Gush after Gush, reserved for you –
Scarlet Experiment! Sceptic Thomas!
Now, do you doubt that your Bird was true?

On a Bird Singing in Its Sleep

A bird half wakened in the lunar noon
Sang halfway through its little inborn tune.
Partly because it sang but once all night
And that from no especial bush's height,
Partly because it sang ventriloquist
And had the inspiration to desist
Almost before the prick of hostile ears.
It ventured less in peril than appears.
It could not have come down to us so far,
Through the interstices of things ajar
On the long bead chain of repeated birth,
To be a bird while we are men on earth,
If singing out of sleep and dream that way
Had made it much more easily a prey.

Sea Mouse

The orphanage of possibility
has had to be expanded to
admit the sea mouse. No one
had asked for such a thing,
or prophesied its advent,

sheltering under ruching
edges of sea lettuce –
a wet thing but pettable
as, seen in the distance,
the tops of copses,

sun-honeyed, needle-pelted
pine trees, bearded barley,
or anything newborn not bald
but furred. No rodent this
scabrous, this unlooked-for

foundling, no catnip plaything
for a cat to worry, not even
an echinoderm, the creature
seems to be a worm. Silk-spiny,
baby-mummy-swaddled, it's

at home where every corridor
is mop-and-bucket scrubbed
and aired from wall to wall
twice daily by the inde-
fatigable tidal head nurse.

from The Seasons

Say, then, where lurk the vast eternal springs
That, like creating Nature, lie concealed
From mortal eye, yet with their lavish stores
Refresh the globe and all its joyous tribes?
O thou pervading genius, given to man
To trace the secrets of the dark abyss!
Oh! lay the mountains bare, and wide display
Their hidden structure to the astonished view;
Strip from the branching Alps their piny load,
The huge incumbrance of horrific woods
From Asian Taurus, from Imaus stretched
Athwart the roving Tartar's sullen bounds;
Give opening Haemus to my searching eye,
And high Olympus pouring many a stream!
Oh, from the sounding summits of the north,
The Dofrine Hills, through Scandinavia rolled
To farthest Lapland and the frozen main;
From lofty Caucasus, far seen by those
Who in the Caspian and black Euxine toil;
From cold Riphaean rocks, which the wild Russ
Believes the stony girdle of the world;
And all the dreadful mountains wrapped in storm
Whence wide Siberia draws her lonely floods;
Oh, sweep the eternal snows! Hung o'er the deep,
That ever works beneath his sounding base,
Bid Atlas, propping heaven, as poets feign,
His subterranean wonders spread! Unveil
The miny caverns, blazing on the day,

Of Abyssinia's cloud-compelling cliffs,
And of the bending Mountains of the Moon!
O'ertopping all these giant-sons of earth,
Let the dire Andes, from the radiant line
Stretched to the stormy seas that thunder round
The Southern Pole, their hideous deeps unfold!
Amazing scene! Behold! the glooms disclose!
I see the rivers in their infant beds!
Deep, deep I hear them labouring to get free!
I see the leaning strata, artful ranged;
The gaping fissures, to receive the rains,
The melting snows, and ever-dripping fogs.
Strowed bibulous above I see the sands,
The pebbly gravel next, the layers then
Of mingled moulds, of more retentive earths,
The guttered rocks and mazy-running clefts,
That, while the stealing moisture they transmit,
Retard its motion, and forbid its waste.
Beneath the incessant weeping of these drains,
I see the rocky siphons stretched immense,
The mighty reservoirs, of hardened chalk
Or stiff compacted clay capacious formed:
O'erflowing thence, the congregated stores,
The crystal treasures of the liquid world,
Through the stirred sands a bubbling passage burst,
And, welling out around the middle steep
Or from the bottoms of the bosomed hills
In pure effusion flow. United thus,
The exhaling sun, the vapour-burdened air,
The gelid mountains, that to rain condensed
These vapours in continual current draw,
And send them o'er the fair-divided earth

In bounteous rivers to the deep again,
A social commerce hold, and firm support
The full-adjusted harmony of things.

On the Ice-islands Seen Floating in the
Germanic Ocean

What portents, from what distant region, ride
Unseen, till now, in ours, th'astonish'd tide?
In ages past, old Proteus with his droves
Of sea-calves sought the mountains and the groves,
But now, descending whence of late they stood,
Themselves the mountains seem to rove the flood.
Dire times were they, full-charged with human woes,
And these scarce less calamitous than those.
What view we now? more wond'rous still! Behold!
Like burnish'd brass they shine, or beaten gold,
And, all around, the pearl's pure splendour show,
And, all around, the ruby's fiery glow.
Come they from India, where the teeming Earth
All-bounteous, gives her richest treasures birth?
And where the costly gems that beam around
The brows of mightiest Potentates abound?
Rapacious hands and ever watchful eyes
Should sooner far have mark'd and seized the prize.
Whence sprang they then? Ejected have they come
From Vesvius' or from Ætna's burning womb?
Thus shine they self-illumed, or but display
The borrow'd splendours of a cloudless day?
With borrow'd beams they shine. The gales that breathe
Now land-ward, and the currents' force beneath
Have borne them nearer, and the nearer sight,
Advantaged more, contemplates them aright.
Their lofty summits crested high they show
With mingled sleet and long-incumbent snow;

The rest is ice. Far hence, where, most severe,
Bleak Winter well-nigh saddens all the year
Their infant growth began. He bade arise
Their uncouth forms, portentous in our eyes.
Oft as, dissolved by transient Suns, the snow
Left the tall cliff to join the flood below,
He caught and curdled with a freezing blast
The current ere it reach'd the boundless waste.
By slow degrees uprose the wond'rous pile,
And long successive ages roll'd the while,
Till, ceaseless in its growth, it claim'd to stand
Tall as its rival mountains on the land.
Thus stood, and, unremoveable by skill
Or force of man, had stood the structure still,
But that, though firmly fixt, supplanted yet
By pressure of its own enormous weight
It left the shelving beach, and with a sound
That shook the bellowing caves and rocks around.
Self-launched and swiftly to the briney wave,
As if instinct with strong desire to lave
Down went the pond'rous mass. So bards have told
How Delos swam th'Ægæan Deep of old.
But not of ice was Delos; Delos bore
Herb, fruit and flow'r; She, crown'd with laurel wore
E'en under wintry skies a summer smile,
And Delos was Apollo's fav'rite isle.
But, horrid wand'rers of the Deep! to you
He deems Cimmerian darkness only due;
Your hated birth he deign'd not to survey,
But, scornful, turn'd his glorious eyes away.
Hence – seek your home – nor longer rashly dare

The darts of Phoebus and a softer air,
Lest ye regret too late your native coast,
In no congenial gulph for ever lost.

JOHN DAVIDSON

Snow

I

'Who affirms that crystals are alive?'
　　I affirm it, let who will deny: –
Crystals are engendered, wax and thrive,
　　Wane and wither; I have seen them die.

Trust me, masters, crystals have their day,
　　Eager to attain the perfect norm,
Lit with purpose, potent to display
　　Facet, angle, colour, beauty, form.

II

Water-crystals need for flower and root
　　Sixty clear degrees, no less, no more;
Snow, so fickle, still in this acute
　　Angle thinks, and learns no other lore:

Such its life, and such its pleasure is,
　　Such its art and traffic, such its gain,
Evermore in new conjunctions this
　　Admirable angle to maintain.

Crystalcraft in every flower and flake
　　Snow exhibits, of the welkin free:
Crystalline are crystals for the sake,
　　All and singular, of crystalry.

Yet does every crystal of the snow
　　Individualize, a seedling sown
Broadcast, but instinct with power to grow
　　Beautiful in beauty of its own.

[77]

Every flake with all its prongs and dints
   Burns ecstatic as a new-lit star:
Men are not more diverse, finger-prints
   More dissimilar than snow-flakes are.

Worlds of men and snow endure, increase,
   Woven of power and passion to defy
Time and travail: only races cease,
   Individual men and crystals die.

III

Jewelled shapes of snow whose feathery showers,
   Fallen or falling wither at a breath,
All afraid are they, and loth as flowers
   Beasts and men to tread the way to death.

Once I saw upon an object-glass,
   Martyred underneath a microscope,
One elaborate snow-flake slowly pass,
   Dying hard, beyond the reach of hope.

Still from shape to shape the crystal changed,
   Writhing in its agony; and still,
Less and less elaborate, arranged
   Potently the angle of its will.

Tortured to a simple final form,
   Angles six and six divergent beams,
Lo, in death it touched the perfect norm
   Verifying all its crystal dreams!

IV

Such the noble tragedy of one
   Martyred snow-flake. Who can tell the fate

[78]

Heinous and uncouth of showers undone,
    Fallen in cities! – showers that expiate

Errant lives from polar worlds adrift
    Where the great millennial snows abide;
Castaways from mountain-chains that lift
    Snowy summits in perennial pride;

Nomad snows, or snows in evil day
    Born to urban ruin, to be tossed,
Trampled, shovelled, ploughed and swept away
    Down the seething sewers: all the frost

Flowers of heaven melted up with lees,
    Offal, recrement, but every flake
Showing to the last in fixed degrees
    Perfect crystals for the crystal's sake.

v

Usefulness of snow is but a chance
    Here in temperate climes with winter sent,
Sheltering earth's prolonged hibernal trance:
    All utility is accident.

Sixty clear degrees the joyful snow,
    Practising economy of means,
Fashions endless beauty in, and so
    Glorifies the universe with scenes

Arctic and antarctic: stainless shrouds,
    Ermine woven in silvery frost, attire
Peaks in every land among the clouds
    Crowned with snows to catch the morning's fire.

from Jubilate Agno

For FRICTION is inevitable because the Universe is FULL of God's works.

For the PERPETUAL MOTION is in all the works of Almighty GOD.

For it is not so in the engines of man, which are made of dead materials, neither indeed can be.

For the Moment of bodies, as it is used, is a false term – bless God ye Speakers on the Fifth of November.

For Time and Weight are by their several estimates.

For I bless GOD in the discovery of the LONGITUDE direct by the means of GLADWICK.

For the motion of the PENDULUM is the longest in that it parries resistance.

For the WEDDING GARMENTS of all men are prepared in the SUN against the day of acceptation.

For the Wedding Garments of all women are prepared in the MOON against the day of their purification.

For CHASTITY is the key of knowledge as in Esdras, Sir Isaac Newton & now, God be praised, in me.

For Newton nevertheless is more of error than of the truth, but I am of the WORD of GOD.

For WATER is not of solid constituents, but is dissolved from precious stones above.

For the life remains in its dissolvent state, and that in great power.

For WATER is condensed by the Lord's FROST, tho' not by the FLORENTINE experiment.

For GLADWICK is a substance growing on hills in the East, candied by the sun, and of diverse colours.

For it is neither stone nor metal but a new creature, soft to
  the ax, but hard to the hammer.
For it answers sundry uses, but particularly it supplies the
  place of Glass.
For it giveth a benign light without the fragility, malignity
  or mischief of glass.
For it attracteth all the colours of the GREAT BOW which is
  fixed in the EAST.
For the FOUNTAINS and SPRINGS are the life of the waters
  working up to God.
For they are in SYMPATHY with the waters above the
  Heavens, which are solid.
For the Fountains, springs and rivers are all of them from
  the sea, whose water is filtrated and purified by the earth.
For is Water above the visible surface in a spiritualizing
  state, which cannot be seen but by application of a
  CAPILLARY TUBE.
For the ASCENT of VAPOURS is the return of thanksgiving
  from all humid bodies.
For the RAIN WATER kept in a reservoir at any altitude,
  suppose of a thousand feet will make a fountain from a
  spout of ten feet of the same height.
For it will ascend in a stream two thirds of the way and
  afterwards prank itself into ten thousand agreeable
  forms.
For the SEA is a seventh of the Earth – the spirit of the Lord
  by Esdras.
For MERCURY is affected by the AIR because it is of a similar
  subtlety.
For the rising in the BAROMETER is not effected by pressure
  but by sympathy.
For it cannot be separated from the creature with which it is
  intimately & eternally connected.

[81]

For where it is stinted of air there it will adhere together &
   stretch on the reverse.
For it works by ballancing according to the hold of the
   spirit.
For QUICK-SILVER is spiritual and so is the AIR to all
   intents and purposes.
For the AIR-PUMP weakens & dispirits but cannot wholly
   exhaust.
For SUCKTION is the withdrawing of the life, but life will
   follow as fast as it can.
For there is infinite provision to keep up the life in all the
   parts of Creation.

PETER REDGROVE

Staines Waterworks

I

So it leaps from your taps like a fish
In its sixth and last purification
It is given a coiling motion
By the final rainbow-painted engines, which thunder;
The water is pumped free through these steel shells
Which are conched like the sea –
This is its release from the long train of events
Called *The Waterworks at Staines.*

II

Riverwater gross as gravy is filtered from
Its coarse detritus at the intake and piped
To the sedimentation plant like an Egyptian nightmare,
For it is a hall of twenty pyramids upside-down
Balanced on their points each holding two hundred and fifty
Thousand gallons making thus the alchemical sign
For water and the female triangle.

III

This reverberates like all the halls
With its engines like some moon rolling
And thundering underneath its floors, for in
This windowless hall of tides we do not see the moon.
Here the last solids fall into that sharp tip
For these twenty pyramids are decanters
And there are strong lights at their points
And when sufficient shadow has gathered the automata

Buttle their muddy jets like a river-milk
Out of the many teats of the water-sign.

IV

In the fourth stage this more spiritual water
Is forced through anthracite beds and treated with poison
    gas,
The verdant chlorine which does not kill it.

V

The habitation of water is a castle, it has turrets
And doors high enough for a mounted knight in armour
To rein in, flourishing his banner, sweating his water,
To gallop along this production line of process where
There are dials to be read as though the castle library –
Books were open on reading-stands at many pages –
But these are automata and the almost-empty halls echo
Emptiness as though you walked the water-conch;
There are very few people in attendance,
All are men and seem very austere
And resemble walking crests of water in their white coats,
Hair white and long in honourable service.

VI

Their cool halls are painted blue and green
Which is the colour of the river in former times,
Purer times, in its flowing rooms.

VII

The final test is a tank of rainbow trout,
The whole station depends on it;
If the fish live, the water is good water.

[84]

In its sixth and last purification
It is given a coiling motion
By vivid yellow and conch-shaped red engines,
This gallery like the broad inside of rainbows
Which rejoice in low thunder over the purification of water,

Trumpeting Staines water triumphantly from spinning
    conches to all taps.

In the Bath

She was interested in prehistory.
It didn't seem so long ago and offered
pleasant notions of a time before civic duty,
when disease was accepted and fought through,
or not. Hers wasn't a museum interest:
it was as tight, neat and uncomplicated
as a reef knot. 'If I came here as a visitor
from Mars, I would be impressed by the water,
the relative health of the inhabitants, the indecent
urge of atoms for complexity – they don't just split
once, think they're clever, and then stop.' She imagined
her body cells spreading like a film to cover the earth,
coating every frond in the tropical rain forest,
every blade of grass on the pampas. Herself
spread thin and making the surface of the world
sparkle. It was a stunning vision of the future.
She lay in the bath with the water touching
her all over, and remembered that not even
the most tender lover could do that. She wondered
if every molecule on the surface of her skin
was wet and what wet meant to such very
tiny matter. To make things worse, or at least
more difficult for the water, she raised her body
slightly, building an island chain of hip bones,
belly, breasts all of which began to dry at once.
She loved the water trails over her body curves,
the classical lines between wet and dry
making graph patterns which she thought might follow

the activity in her brain – all she wanted
was to be a good atlas, a bright school map
to shine up the world for everyone to see.

Lay of the Trilobite

A mountain's giddy height I sought,
  Because I could not find
Sufficient vague and mighty thought
  To fill my mighty mind;
And as I wandered ill at ease,
  There chanced upon my sight
A native of Silurian seas,
  An ancient Trilobite.

So calm, so peacefully he lay,
  I watched him even with tears:
I thought of Monads far away
  In the forgotten years.
How wonderful it seemed and right,
  The providential plan,
That he should be a Trilobite,
  And I should be a Man!

And then, quite natural and free
  Out of his rocky bed,
That Trilobite he spoke to me
  And this is what he said:
'I don't know how the thing was done,
  Although I cannot doubt it;
But Huxley – he if anyone
  Can tell you all about it;

'How all your faiths are ghosts and dreams,
  How in the silent sea
Your ancestors were Monotremes –
  Whatever these may be;

How you evolved your shining lights
    Of wisdom and perfection
From Jelly-fish and Trilobites
    By Natural Selection.

'You've Kant to make your brains go round,
    Hegel you have to clear them,
You've Mr Browning to confound,
    And Mr Punch to cheer them!
The native of an alien land
    You call a man and brother,
And greet with hymn-book in one hand
    And pistol in the other!

'You've Politics to make you fight
    As if you were possessed:
You've cannon and you've dynamite
    To give the nations rest:
The side that makes the loudest din
    Is surest to be right,
And oh, a pretty fix you're in!'
    Remarked the Trilobite.

'But gentle, stupid, free from woe
    I lived among my nation,
I didn't care – I didn't know
    That I was a Crustacean.*
I didn't grumble, didn't steal,
    I *never* took to rhyme:
Salt water was my frugal meal,
    And carbonate of lime.'

Reluctantly I turned away,
    No other word he said;
An ancient Trilobite, he lay

[89]

Within his rocky bed.
I did not answer him, for that
    Would have annoyed my pride:
I merely bowed, and raised my hat,
    But in my heart I cried: –

'I wish our brains were not so good,
    I wish our skulls were thicker,
I wish that Evolution could
    Have stopped a little quicker;
For oh, it was a happy plight,
    Of liberty and ease,
To be a simple Trilobite
    In the Silurian seas!'

*He was not a Crustacean. He has since discovered that he was an Arachnid, or something similar. But he says it does not matter. He says they told him wrong once, and they may again [Kendall's note].

The Fish in the Stone

The fish in the stone
would like to fall
back into the sea.

He is weary
of analysis, the small
predictable truths.
He is weary of waiting
in the open,
his profile stamped
by a white light.

In the ocean the silence
moves and moves

and so much is unnecessary!
Patient, he drifts
until the moment comes
to cast his
skeletal blossom.

The fish in the stone
knows to fail is
to do the living
a favor.

He knows why the ant
engineers a gangster's
funeral, garish
and perfectly amber.
He knows why the scientist

[91]

in secret delight
strokes the fern's
voluptuous braille.

Of many Worlds in this World

Just like as in a *Nest* of *Boxes* round,
Degrees of Sizes in each Box are found:
So, in this *World*, may many others be
Thinner and less, and less still by degree:
Although they are not subject to our *sense*,
A World may be no bigger than *Two-pence*.
NATURE is curious, and such Works may shape,
Which our dull *senses* easily escape:
For *Creatures*, small as *Atoms*, may be there,
If every one a *Creature's Figure* bear.
If *Atoms Four*, a *World* can make, then see
What several *Worlds* might in an *Ear-ring* be:
For, Millions of those *Atoms* may be in
The Head of one small, little, single *Pin*.
And if thus small, then *Ladies* may well wear
A *World* of *Worlds*, as *Pendents* in each *Ear*.

from Greatness in Little

What *Skill* is in the *frame* of *Insects* shown?
How *fine* the *Threds*, in their *small Textures* spun?
How *close* those *Instruments* and *Engines* knit,
Which *Motion*, and their *slender Sense* transmit?
Like *living Watches*, each of these conceals
A thousand *Springs of Life*, and *moving wheels*.
Each *Ligature* a *Lab'rynth* seems, each *part*
All *wonder* is, all *Workmanship* and *Art*.

    Rather let me this *little Greatness* know,
Then all the *Mighty Acts* of *Great Ones* do.
These *Engines* understand, rather than prove
An *Archimedes*, and the *Earth* remove.
These *Atom-Worlds* found out, I would despise
Columbus, and his vast *Discoveries*.

Design

I found a dimpled spider, fat and white,
On a white heal-all, holding up a moth
Like a white piece of rigid satin cloth –
Assorted characters of death and blight
Mixed ready to begin the morning right,
Like the ingredients of a witches' broth –
A snow-drop spider, a flower like a froth,
And dead wings carried like a paper kite.

What had that flower to do with being white,
The wayside blue and innocent heal-all?
What brought the kindred spider to that height,
Then steered the white moth thither in the night?
What but design of darkness to appall? –
If design govern in a thing so small.

In the Likeness of a Grasshopper

A trap
Waits on the field path.

A wicker contraption, with working parts,
Its spring tensed and set.

So flimsily made, out of grass
(Out of the stems, the joints, the raspy-dry flags).

Baited with a fur-soft caterpillar,
A belly of amorous life, pulsing signals.

Along comes a love-sick, perfume-footed
Music of the wild earth.

The trap, touched by a breath,
Jars into action, its parts blur –

And music cries out.

A sinewy violin
Has caught its violinist.

Cloud-fingered summer, the beautiful trapper,
Picks up the singing cage

And takes out the Song, adds it to the Songs
With which she robes herself, which are her wealth,

Sets her trap again, a yard further on.

EDWARD TAYLOR

Upon a Wasp Chilled with Cold

The Bear that breaths the Northern blast
Did numb, Torpedo-like, a Wasp
Whose stiffend limbs encrampt, lay bathing
In Sol's warm breath and shine as saving,
Which with her hands she chafes and slams
Rubbing her Legs, Shanks, Thighs, and hands.
Her petty toes, and fingers ends
Nipt with this breath, she out extends
Unto the sun, in greate desire
To warm her digits at that fire:
Doth hold her Temples in this state
Where pulse doth beate, and head doth ake:
Doth turn and stretch her body small,
Doth comb her velvet capitall
As if her little brain-pan were
A Volume of choice precepts cleare:
As if her sattin jacket hot
Contained Apothecaries Shop
Of Natures recepts, that prevails
To remedy all her sad ailes,
As if her velvet helmet high
Did turret rationality.
She fans her wing up to the winde
As if her Pettycoate were lin'de
With reasons fleece, and hoises saile
And humming flies in thankfull gaile
Unto her dun curld palace Hall,
Her warm thanks offering for all.

[97]

Lord, cleare my misted sight that I
May hence view thy Divinity,
Some sparkes whereof thou up dost hasp
Within this little downy Wasp,
In whose small Corporation wee
A school and a schoolmaster see:
Where we may learn, and easily finde
A nimble Spirit, bravely minde
Her worke in ev'ry limb: and lace
It up neate with a vitall grace,
Acting each part though ne'er so small,
Here of this fustian animall,
Till I enravisht climb into
The Godhead on this ladder doe:
Where all my pipes inspir'de upraise
An Heavenly musick, furr'd with praise.

At It

I think he sits at that strange table
of Eddington's, that is not a table
at all, but nodes and molecules
pushing against molecules
and nodes; and he writes there
in invisible handwriting the instructions
the genes follow. I imagine his
face that is more the face
of a clock, and the time told by it
is now, though Greece is referred
to and Egypt and empires
not yet begun.
                    And I would have
things to say to this God
at the judgement, storming at him,
as Job stormed with the eloquence
of the abused heart. But there will be
no judgement other than the verdict
of his calculations, that abstruse
geometry that proceeds eternally
in the silence beyond right and wrong.

from An Essay on Man

Know then thyself, presume not God to scan;
The proper study of Mankind is Man.
Plac'd on this isthmus of a middle state,
A being darkly wise, and rudely great:
With too much knowledge for the Sceptic side,
With too much weakness for the Stoic's pride,
He hangs between; in doubt to act, or rest,
In doubt to deem himself a God, or Beast;
In doubt his Mind or Body to prefer,
Born but to die, and reas'ning but to err;
Alike in ignorance, his reason such,
Whether he thinks too little, or too much:
Chaos of Thought and Passion, all confus'd;
Still by himself abus'd, or disabus'd;
Created half to rise, and half to fall;
Great lord of all things, yet a prey to all;
Sole judge of Truth, in endless Error hurl'd:
The glory, jest, and riddle of the world!

   Go, wond'rous creature! mount where Science guides
Go, measure earth, weigh air, and state the tides;
Instruct the planets in what orbs to run,
Correct old Time, and regulate the Sun;
Go, soar with Plato to th' empyreal sphere,
To the first good, first perfect, and first fair;
Or tread the mazy round his follow'rs trod,
And quitting sense call imitating God;
As Eastern priests in giddy circles run,
And turn their heads to imitate the Sun.
Go, teach Eternal Wisdom how to rule –

Then drop into thyself, and be a fool!
  Superior beings, when of late they saw
A mortal Man unfold all Nature's law,
Admir'd such wisdom in an earthly shape,
And shew'd a NEWTON as we shew an Ape.
  Could he, whose rules the rapid Comet bind,
Describe or fix one movement of his Mind?
Who saw its fires here rise, and there descend,
Explain his own beginning, or his end?
Alas what wonder! Man's superior part
Uncheck'd may rise, and climb from art to art:
But when his own great work is but begun,
What Reason weaves, by Passion is undone.
  Trace Science then, with Modesty thy guide;
First strip off all her equipage of Pride,
Deduct what is but Vanity, or Dress,
Or Learning's Luxury, or Idleness;
Or tricks to shew the stretch of human brain,
Mere curious pleasure, or ingenious pain:
Expunge the whole, or lop th' excrescent parts
Of all, our Vices have created Arts:
Then see how little the remaining sum,
Which serv'd the past, and must the times to come!

Science

Then it was the future, though what's arrived
isn't what we had in mind, all chrome and
cybernetics, when we set up exhibits
in the cafeteria for the judges
to review what we'd made of our hypotheses.

The class skeptic (he later refused to sign
anyone's yearbook, calling it a sentimental
degradation of language) chloroformed mice,
weighing the bodies before and after
to catch the weight of the soul,

wanting to prove the invisible
real as a bagful of nails. A girl
who knew it all made cookies from euglena,
a one-celled compromise between animal and plant,
she had cultured in a flask.

We're smart enough, she concluded,
to survive our mistakes, showing photos of farmland,
poisoned, gouged, eroded. No one believed
he really had built it when a kid no one knew
showed up with an atom smasher, confirming that

the tiniest particles could be changed
into something even harder to break.
And one whose mother had cancer (hard to admit now,
it was me) distilled the tar of cigarettes
to paint it on the backs of shaven mice.

She wanted to know what it took,
a little vial of sure malignancy,

to prove a daily intake smaller
than a single aspirin could finish
something as large as a life. I thought of this

because, today, the dusky seaside sparrow
became extinct. It may never be as famous
as the pterodactyl or the dodo,
but the last one died today, a resident
of Walt Disney World where now its tissue samples

lie frozen, in case someday we learn to clone
one from a few cells. Like those instant dinosaurs
that come in a gelatin capsule – just add water
and they inflate. One other thing this
brings to mind. The euglena girl won first prize

both for science and, I think, in retrospect, for hope.

The Mad Cow Talks Back

I'm not mad. It just seems that way
because I stagger and get a bit irritable.
There are wonderful holes in my brain
through which ideas from outside can travel
at top speed and through which voices,
sometimes whole people, speak to me
about the universe. Most brains are too
compressed. You need this spongy
generosity to let the others in.

I love the staggers. Suddenly the surface
of the world is ice and I'm a magnificent
skater turning and spinning across whole hard
Pacifics and Atlantics. It's risky when
you're good, so of course the legs go before,
behind, and to the side of the body from time
to time, and then there's the general embarrassing
collapse, but when that happens it's glorious
because it's always when you're travelling
most furiously in your mind. My brain's like
the hive: constant little murmurs from its cells
saying this is the way, this is the way to go.

Still Life

The bullet has almost entered the brain:
I can feel it sprint down the gun barrel,
rolling each bevel around like a hoop
on a pigslide of calibrated steel and oil.
Now it whistles free and aloft
in that ice-cold millimeter of air,
then boils as the first layer of skin
shales off like ragged leaves of soap.
The trigger's omnipresent click
makes triggers all over the body fire.
Now it tunnels through palisades,
veins, arteries, white corpuscles
red and battered as swollen ghosts,
cuts the struts on a glacial bone
jutting out like the leg of a single flamingo,
feints and draws in close for the kill,
egged on by a mouse-gray parliament of cells.

The Cloud Chamber
for N.C. 1951–72

'You crack an atom, what's left? Particles,
bits. It's like Meccano: proton, neutron, quark.
Don't you see . . . ?'
                         The things you knew.
The rest of us set our horizons at the girls'
school down the road. Whatever you
dreamed of, you left us in the dark.
('I couldn't follow him,' one friend confessed
after the fact, then '*Why?* The waste, the waste!'
then again 'Did he *know* something we don't?')

'. . . there's nothing to it,' your pale face
lit on a smile. 'A molecule? A galaxy?
Nothing but little obstacles in space.'
As clear as mud. Just for a moment, though,
your laughter shook me. It was wild –
a touch of vertigo. I saw the solid world
come unput at our feet. I didn't see

the logic: how you would leave behind
friends, family, a fixed address,
even your books, until
                         one tactful line
in the *Hatched-Matched-&-Despatched*: DIED
SUDDENLY. No note, no clue,
you left us nothing, as if we were less
than nothing (little obstacles?) to you.
'*Why?*' You'd have shrugged; worse, smiled.

'Why anything?' What could I say?
Except . . . that icy-crisp November night
we watched for meteors, crouched back to back
for warmth. 'There!'
                              'Where?'
                                         'Too late.'
A scatter-fall of debris from deep space.
I felt you shivering. I saw the track
in the cloud chamber. Bits. The waste.
The toll of microseconds. Particle decay.

Cloud chamber: an apparatus in which the path of charged particles is made visible
(Chambers Dictionary)

Curie

Radium is my element.
My complexion has taken on the warm glow
of an experimental tint.

My hands display
chemical burns, nails
broken like brittle kindling. The X-ray

is another name for my eyes.
Shield yourself or let them show you
how far below the surface beauty lies

like a molten core, magmatic rock bed
from which a spark is sometimes struck
turning lava into lead,

my poor philosopher's stone.
A modest miracle, but one
admirable in woman.

LAVINIA GREENLAW

The Innocence of Radium

With a head full of Swiss clockmakers,
she took a job at a New Jersey factory
painting luminous numbers, copying the style
believed to be found in the candlelit backrooms
of snowbound alpine villages.

Holding each clockface to the light,
she would catch a glimpse of the chemist
as he measured and checked. He was old enough,
had a kind face and a foreign name
she never dared to pronounce: Sochocky.

For a joke she painted her teeth and nails,
jumped out on the other girls walking home.
In bed that night she laughed out loud
and stroked herself with ten green fingertips.
Unable to sleep, the chemist traced each number

on the face he had stolen from the factory floor.
He liked the curve of her eights;
the way she raised the wet brush to her lips
and, with a delicate purse of her mouth,
smoothed the bristle to a perfect tip.

Over the years he watched her grow dull.
The doctors gave up, removed half her jaw,
and blamed syphilis when her thighbone snapped
as she struggled up a flight of steps.
Diagnosing infidelity, the chemist pronounced

the innocence of radium, a kind of radiance
that could not be held by the body of a woman,

[109]

only caught between her teeth. He was proud
of his paint and made public speeches
on how it could be used by artists to convey

the quality of moonlight. Sochocky displayed
these shining landscapes on his walls;
his faith sustained alone in a room
full of warm skies that broke up the dark
and drained his blood of its colour.

His dangerous bones could not keep their secret.
Laid out for X-ray, before a single button was pressed,
they exposed the plate and pictured themselves
as a ghost, not a skeleton, a photograph
he was unable to stop being developed and fixed.

PETER REDGROVE

The Visible Baby

A large transparent baby like a skeleton in a red tree,
Like a little skeleton in the rootlet-pattern;
He is not of glass, this baby, his flesh is see-through,
Otherwise he is quite the same as any other baby.

I can see the white caterpillar of his milk looping through
    him,
I can see the pearl-bubble of his wind and stroke it out of him,
I can see his little lungs breathing like pink parks of trees,
I can see his little brain in its glass case like a budding rose;

There are his teeth in his transparent gums like a budding
    hawthorn twig,
His eyes like open poppies follow the light,
His tongue is like a crest of his thumping blood,
His heart like two squirrels one scarlet, one purple
Mating in the canopy of a blood-tree;

His spine like a necklace, all silvery-strung with cartilages,
His handbones like a working-party of white insects,
His nerves like a tree of ice with sunlight shooting through it,

What a closed book bound in wrinkled illustrations his
    father is to him!

Shadows in the Water

In unexperienc'd Infancy
Many a sweet Mistake doth ly:
Mistake, tho false, intending tru;
A *Seeming* somwhat more than *View*;
   That doth instruct the Mind
   In Things that ly behind,
And many Secrets to us show
Which afterwards we com to know.

Thus did I by the Water's brink
Another World beneath me think;
And while the lofty spacious Skies
Reversed there abus'd mine Eys,
   I fancy'd other Feet
   Came mine to touch or meet;
As by som Puddle I did play
Another World within it lay.

Beneath the Water Peeple drown'd,
Yet with another Hev'n crown'd,
In spacious Regions seem'd to go
As freely moving to and fro:
   In bright and open Space
   I saw their very face;
Eys, Hands, and Feet they had like mine;
Another Sun did with them shine.

'Twas strange that Peeple there should walk,
And yet I could not hear them talk:
That throu a little watry Chink,
Which one dry Ox or Horse might drink,

We other Worlds should see,
　　Yet not admitted be;
And other Confines there behold
Of Light and Darkness, Heat and Cold.

I call'd them oft, but call'd in vain;
No Speeches we could entertain:
Yet did I there expect to find
Som other World, to pleas my Mind.
　　I plainly saw by these
　　A new *Antipodes*,
Whom, tho they were so plainly seen,
A Film kept off that stood between.

By walking Men's reversed Feet
I chanc'd another World to meet;
Tho it did not to View exceed
A Phantasm, 'tis a World indeed,
　　Where Skies beneath us shine,
　　And Earth by Art divine
Another face presents below,
Where Peeple's feet against Ours go.

Within the Regions of the Air,
Compass'd about with Hev'ns fair,
Great Tracts of Land there may be found
Enricht with Fields and fertil Ground;
　　Where many num'rous Hosts,
　　In those far distant Coasts,
For other great and glorious Ends,
Inhabit, my yet unknown Friends.

O ye that stand upon the Brink,
Whom I so near me, throu the Chink,
With Wonder see: What Faces there,

[113]

Whose Feet, whose Bodies, do ye wear?
 I my Companions see
 In You, another Me.
They seemed Others, but are We;
Our second Selvs those Shadows be.

Look how far off those lower Skies
Extend themselves! scarce with mine Eys
I can them reach. O ye my Friends,
What *Secret* borders on those Ends?
 Are lofty Hevens hurl'd
 'Bout your inferior World?
Are ye the Representatives
Of other Peopl's distant Lives?

Of all the Play-mates which I knew
That here I do the Image view
In other Selvs; what can it mean?
But that below the purling Stream
 Som unknown Joys there be
 Laid up in Store for me;
To which I shall, when that thin Skin
Is broken, be admitted in.

Reflections

The mirror above my fireplace reflects the reflected
Room in my window; I look in the mirror at night
And see two rooms, the first where left is right
And the second, beyond the reflected window, corrected
But there I am standing back to my back. The standard
Lamp comes thrice in my mirror, twice in my window,
The fire in the mirror lies two rooms away through the
    window,
The fire in the window lies one room away down the
    terrace,
My actual room stands sandwiched between confections
Of night and lights and glass and in both directions
I can see beyond and through the reflections the street
    lamps
At home outdoors where my indoors rooms lie stranded,
Where a taxi perhaps will drive in through the bookcase
Whose books are not for reading and past the fire
Which gives no warmth and pull up by my desk
At which I cannot write since I am not lefthanded.

Monet Refuses the Operation

Doctor, you say there are no haloes
around the streetlights in Paris
and what I see is an aberration
caused by old age, an affliction.
I tell you it has taken me all my life
to arrive at the vision of gas lamps as angels,
to soften and blur and finally banish
the edges you regret I don't see,
to learn that the line I called the horizon
does not exist and sky and water,
so long apart, are the same state of being.
Fifty-four years before I could see
Rouen cathedral is built
of parallel shafts of sun,
and now you want to restore
my youthful errors: fixed
notions of top and bottom,
the illusion of three-dimensional space,
wisteria separate
from the bridge it covers.
What can I say to convince you
the Houses of Parliament dissolve
night after night to become
the fluid dream of the Thames?
I will not return to a universe
of objects that don't know each other,
as if islands were not the lost children
of one great continent. The world
is flux, and light becomes what it touches,

becomes water, lilies on water,
above and below water,
becomes lilac and mauve and yellow
and white and cerulean lamps,
small fists passing sunlight
so quickly to one another
that it would take long, streaming hair
inside my brush to catch it.
To paint the speed of light!
Our weighted shapes, these verticals,
burn to mix with air
and change our bones, skin, clothes
to gases. Doctor,
if only you could see
how heaven pulls earth into its arms
and how infinitely the heart expands
to claim this world, blue vapor without end.

Modes of Representation

If you look in old chemistry books
you see
all those line cuts
of laboratory experiments
in cross-section.
The sign for water
is a containing line, the meniscus
(which rarely curls up the walls of the beaker),
and below it
a sea
of straight horizontal dashes
carefully unaligned vertically.
Every cork or rubber stopper
is cutaway.
You can see inside
every vessel
without reflections, without getting wet,
and explore every kink
in a copper condenser.
Flames are outlined cypresses
or a tulip at dawn,
and some Klee arrows
help to move gases and liquids the right way.
Sometimes a disembodied hand
holds up a flask.
Sometimes there is an unblinking observer's eye.
Around 1920
photoengraving
became economically feasible

and took over.
Seven-story distillation columns
(polished up for the occasion),
like giant clarinets,
rose in every text, along
with heaps of chemicals, eventually in color.
Suddenly
water and glass, all reflection
became difficult.
One had to worry about light,
about the sex
and length of dress or cut of suit
of the person sitting at the controls of this impressive
    instrument.
Car models and hairstyles
dated the books more
than the chemistry in them.
Around that time
teachers noted a deterioration
in the students' ability to follow
a simple experimental procedure.

Tested

The test we do is simple. It was tested
In the laboratories where such tests take place.
Reactions have been measured, noted, tested.

The aperture is touched. We do the touching.
Dilation follows from the touch we give.
What follows is so simple that it's touching.

Arousal as reaction is what's normal
And that reaction is the one we want.
Once that is known, the whole thing is quite normal.

Even the youngest show the same reaction
As older ones who recognise the sign.
Our touch expects a uniform reaction.

And so our tests have proved how very simple
The mechanism is that proves the crime.
What follows may be hard. But this is simple.

EDWIN MORGAN

Pleasures of a Technological University

magnesium and Crashaw
semiotics and ergonomics
lasers and caesuras
retro-rockets and peripeteia
sapphics and turquoise
sines and sememes
hubris and helium
Eliot and entropy
enjambment and switchgear
quasars and hapax legomena
thermodynamics and macrostylistics
anti-hero and anti-matter
bubble chambers and E. K. Chambers
H_2O and 8vo
genres and genera
meters and metres
litmus and anagnorisis
DNA and ABBA
DNB and TNT
bleeps and feet
Rhine and Poe
ficelle and cantilever
metal fatigue and dead metaphors
flyting and teratology
ergs and Bacon
genes and fitts
morphs and mesons
tektites and données
Möbius's ring and Freytag's pyramid

stichomythia and feedback
red shifts and Tam o'Shanter
copula and cupola
sonic booms and euphuism
osmosis and entasis
umlaut and ohm
Ethan Brand and ethyl fluid
wit and sodium chloride
neoaristotelianism and microminiaturization
F_3 and Fe
poem and pome

Möbius Strip-Tease

An erudite demon, a fiend in topology,
Shaped much like a grin on a sphere on a trivet,
To add to the carnal advancement of knowledge he
Invented a woman. Now, would you believe it?

A woman so modelled no man could resist her,
So luscious her curves, so alluring her smile,
Yet no daughter of Eve's could claim her for sister,
Though equally formed to seduce and beguile.

For her surface – a pure aphrodisiac plastic –
No mathematician could ever equate
By any contortion or motion elastic
To those we caress in man's fallen estate.

O she was a heartache! O she was a honey!
The fiend asked his friends gathered round in a ring:
'A degenerate set! Would you bet even money,
Though she looks like a succubus fit for a King?'

'Come off it,' they answered, 'her shape is a woman's,
So she can't be a true topological freak,
Though a singleton, maybe, to ordinary humans
Who think any girl they adore is unique.'

'In our rubber sheet world,' said the fiend with a chortle
Converting himself to a three-masted barque,
'Equivalent shapes may delude a poor mortal,
But *you* should know Woman's distinguishing mark.'

'A woman's a man-trap,' they answered in chorus,
'A trochus with trunnions, a tunnel to Hell;

Reduced to essentials she's simply a torus
And this must apply to your temptress as well.'

'Alas, my poor friends you are sadly mistaken:
This exquisite creature is built to deceive;
For the Devil's own cunning will not save his bacon
When caught in the nets that topologists weave.

'This marvellous manifold's not like a doughnut,
Quoit or cat's-cradle or twists of red tape,
And though very tortive, she screws like no known nut;
So I'd better explain her remarkable shape.

'Like a Boy Surface girl, my delightful invention
In Euclidean space is too awkward to plot,
But in Hell, with the help of an extra dimension
And a regressive cut, she's a true-lovers'-knot,

'Though she looks like a woman from thrutch-piece to
    throttle,
If you follow my clew of a Möbius strip-tease,
She is really a camouflaged double Klein bottle
With only one surface unlike other shes.

'Four Möbius strips brought my plan to fruition,
Ingeniously joined by original sin;
If you rise to the urgings of male intuition,
You'll find yourself out every time you go in.

'She cannot be mated or orientated,
Nor is homeomorphic to any known male;
And though in her arms you may feel quite elated,
All further advances are destined to fail.

'And before we proceed to our first Demon-stration,
May I venture to say, with excusable pride,

That this elegant essay in total frustration
Justifies mathematics, both pure and applied.

'Furthermore, as a torment for sinful seducers,
I think I may claim for the very first time,
To have added to Hell's repertoire something new, sirs:
A case where the punishment *won't* fit the crime.'

Homage to Gödel

'Pull yourself out of the mire
by your own hair': Münchausen's theorem
is charming, but do not forget:
the Baron was a great liar.

Gödel's theorem may seem, at first sight,
rather nondescript,
but please keep in mind:
Gödel is right.

'In any sufficiently rich system
statements are possible
which can neither be proved
nor refuted within the system,
unless the system itself
is inconsistent.'

You can describe your own language
in your own language:
but not quite.
You can investigate your own brain
by means of your own brain:
but not quite.
Etc.

In order to be vindicated
any conceivable system
must transcend, and that means,
destroy itself.

'Sufficiently rich' or not:
Freedom from contradiction

is either a deficiency symptom,
or it amounts to a contradiction.

(Certainty = Inconsistency.)

Any conceivable horseman,
including Münchausen,
including yourself, is a subsystem
of a sufficiently rich mire.

And a subsystem of this subsystem
is your own hair,
favourite tackle
of reformists and liars.

In any sufficiently rich system
including the present mire
statements are possible
which can neither be proved
nor refuted within the system.

Those are the statements
to grasp, and pull!

translated by the author

CHRISTOPHER REID

Amphibiology

Like old men frolicking in sacks
seals slither on the sea-thrashed rocks.

Why does their melancholy sport
exert such a strong pull on my heart?

I could stand here for hours on end
watching them fail to make dry land.

From time to time one gains brief purchase,
adopting the pose of a Grand Duchess.

In seconds, though, a fist of surf
rises to swipe the pretender off.

Repetitive slapstick, it has the charm
of earliest documentary film.

Stuffed statesmen and wind-up warriors
turn to salute us across the years . . .

Only, in this case, something far
more ancient seems to hang in the air.

It could be the question, whether to plump
for a great evolutionary jump

or stay put in the icy brine.
May the good Lord send them a hopeful sign!

The Naked Ape

*(following, perhaps all too closely, Desmond Morris's
anthropological revelations)*

The dinosaur died, and small
   Insectivores (how gruesome!) crawled
From bush to tree, from bug to bud,
   From spider-diet to forest fruit and nut,
Forming bioptic vision and
     The grasping hand.

These perfect monkeys then were faced
   With shrinking groves; the challenged race,
De-Edenized by glacial whim,
   Sent forth from its arboreal cradle him
Who engineered himself to run
     With deer and lion –

The 'naked ape.' Why naked? Well,
   Upon those meaty plains, that *veldt*
Of prey, as pell-mell they competed
   With cheetahs, hairy primates overheated;
Selection pressure, just though cruel,
     Favored the cool.

Unlikeliest of hunters, nude
   And weak and tardy to mature,
This ill-cast carnivore attacked,
   With weapons he invented, *in a pack*.
The tribe was born. To set men free,
     The family

Evolved; monogamy occurred.
    The female – sexually alert
Throughout the month, equipped to have
    Pronounced orgasms – perpetrated love.
The married state decreed its *lex*
    Privata: sex.

And Nature, pandering, bestowed
    On virgin ears erotic lobes
And hung on women hemispheres
    That imitate their once-attractive rears:
A social animal disarms
    With frontal charms.

All too erogenous, the ape
    To give his lusts a decent shape
Conceived the cocktail party, where
    Unmates refuse to touch each other's hair
And make small 'grooming' talk instead
    Of going to bed.

He drowns his body scents in baths
    And if, in some conflux of paths,
He bumps another, says, 'Excuse
    Me, *please*.' He suffers rashes and subdues
Aggressiveness by making fists
    And laundry lists,

Suspension bridges, aeroplanes,
    And charts that show biweekly gains
And losses. Noble animal!
    To try to lead on this terrestrial ball,
With grasping hand and saucy wife,
    The upright life.

Heredity

I am the family face;
Flesh perishes, I live on,
Projecting trait and trace
Through time to times anon,
And leaping from place to place
Over oblivion.

The years-heired feature that can
In curve and voice and eye
Despise the human span
Of durance – that is I;
The eternal thing in man,
That heeds no call to die.

ALFRED, LORD TENNYSON

from In Memoriam

LIV

The wish, that of the living whole
    No life may fail beyond the grave,
    Derives it not from what we have
The likest God within the soul?

Are God and Nature then at strife,
    That Nature lends such evil dreams?
    So careful of the type she seems,
So careless of the single life;

That I, considering everywhere
    Her secret meaning in her deeds,
    And finding that of fifty seeds
She often brings but one to bear,

I falter where I firmly trod,
    And falling with my weight of cares
    Upon the great world's altar-stairs
That slope thro' darkness up to God,

I stretch lame hands of faith, and grope,
    And gather dust and chaff, and call
    To what I feel is Lord of all,
And faintly trust the larger hope.

LV

'So careful of the type?' but no.
    From scarped cliff and quarried stone
    She cries 'A thousand types are gone:
I care for nothing, all shall go.

Thou makest thine appeal to me:
    I bring to life, I bring to death:
    The spirit does but mean the breath:
I know no more.' And he, shall he,

Man, her last work, who seem'd so fair,
    Such splendid purpose in his eyes,
    Who roll'd the psalm to wintry skies,
Who built him fanes of fruitless prayer,

Who trusted God was love indeed
    And love Creation's final law –
    Tho' Nature, red in tooth and claw
With ravine, shriek'd against his creed –

Who loved, who suffer'd countless ills,
    Who battled for the True, the Just,
    Be blown about the desert dust,
Or seal'd within the iron hills?

No more? A monster then, a dream,
    A discord. Dragons of the prime,
    That tare each other in their slime,
Were mellow music match'd with him.

O life as futile, then, as frail!
    O for thy voice to soothe and bless!
    What hope of answer, or redress?
Behind the veil, behind the veil.

CXVII

Contemplate all this work of Time,
    The giant labouring in his youth;
    Nor dream of human love and truth,
As dying Nature's earth and lime;

[133]

But trust that those we call the dead
    Are breathers of an ampler day
    For ever nobler ends. They say,
The solid earth whereon we tread

In tracts of fluent heat began,
    And grew to seeming-random forms,
    The seeming prey of cyclic storms,
Till at the last arose the man;

Who throve and branch'd from clime to clime,
    The herald of a higher race,
    And of himself in higher place,
If so he type this work of time

Within himself, from more to more;
    Or, crown'd with attributes of woe
    Like glories, move his course, and show
That life is not as idle ore,

But iron dug from central gloom,
    And heated hot with burning fears,
    And dipt in baths of hissing tears,
And batter'd with the shocks of doom

To shape and use. Arise and fly
    The reeling Faun, the sensual feast;
    Move upward, working out the beast,
And let the ape and tiger die.

CXIX

I trust I have not wasted breath:
    I think we are not wholly brain,
    Magnetic mockeries; not in vain,
Like Paul with beasts, I fought with Death;

Not only cunning casts in clay:
    Let Science prove we are, and then
    What matters Science unto men,
At least to me? I would not stay.

Let him, the wiser man who springs
    Hereafter, up from childhood shape
    His action like the greater ape,
But I was born to other things.

from A Drunk Man Looks at the Thistle

What better's a forhooied nest
Than skasloch scattered owre the grund?

O hard it is for man to ken
He's no creation's goal nor yet
A benefitter by't at last –
A means to ends he'll never ken,
And as to michtier elements
The slauchtered brutes he eats to him
Or form o life owre smaa to see
Wi which his heedless body swarms,
And aa man's thocht nae mair to them
Than ony mousewob to a man,
His Heaven to them the blinterin o
A snail-trail on their closet waa!

For what's an atom o a twig
That taks a billion to an inch
To aa the routh o shoots that mak
The bygrowth o the Earth about
The michty trunk o Space that spreids
Ramel o licht that hae nae end,
– The trunk wi centuries for rings,
Comets for fruit, November shouers
For leafs that in its Autumns faa
– And Man at maist o sic a twig
Ane o the countless atoms is!

My sinnens and my veins are but
As muckle o a single shoot,
Whas fibres I can ne'er unwaft

[136]

O my wife's flesh and mither's flesh
And aa the flesh o humankind
And revelled thrums o beasts and plants,
As gangs to mak twixt birth and daith
Ae sliver for a microscope;
And aa the life o Earth to be
Can never lift frae underneath
The shank o which our destiny's pairt
As heich's to stand forenenst the trunk
Stupendous as a windlestrae!

I'm under nae delusions, fegs!
The whuppan souker at whas tip
Our little point o view appears,
A midget coom o continents
Wi blebs o oceans set, sends up
The braith o daith as weel as life,
And we maun braird anither tip
Out owre us or we wither tae,
And join the sentrice skeleton
As coral insects big their reefs.

What is the tree? As fer as Man's
Concerned it disna maitter
Gin but a giant thistle 'tis
That spreids eternal mischief there,
As I'm inclined to think.
Ruthless it sends its solid growth
Through mair than he can e'er conceive,
And braks his warlds abreid and rives
His Heavens to tatters on its horns.

The nature or the purpose o't
He needna fash to speir, for he

Is destined to be sune owre grown
And hidden wi the parent wud
The spreidan boughs in darkness hap,
And aa its future life'll be
Outwith'm as he's outwith his banes.

owre smaa, *too small*; mousewob, *spider's web*; blinterin, *glistening*; waa, *wall*;
routh, *quantity*; ramel, *branches*; sinnens, *sinews*; muckle, *much*; unwaft,
unweave; revelled thrums, *ravelled threads*; Ae, *One*; heich, *high*; forenenst, *in
relation to*; windlestrae, *straw*; whuppan souker, *whopping sucker (of a tree)*;
coom, *comb*; blebs, *drops*; braird, *sprout*; maun, *must*; sentrice, *scaffold-like*;
big, *build*; abreid, *asunder*; rives, *tears*; fash to speir, *trouble to ask*; wud, *wood*;
hap, *cover*; outwith, *outside*

RICHARD WILBUR

Seed Leaves
homage to R. F.

Here something stubborn comes,
Dislodging the earth crumbs
And making crusty rubble.
It comes up bending double,
And looks like a green staple.
It could be seedling maple,
Or artichoke, or bean.
That remains to be seen.

Forced to make choice of ends,
The stalk in time unbends,
Shakes off the seed-case, heaves
Aloft, and spreads two leaves
Which still display no sure
And special signature.
Toothless and fat, they keep
The oval form of sleep.

This plant would like to grow
And yet be embryo;
Increase, and yet escape
The doom of taking shape;
Be vaguely vast, and climb
To the tip end of time
With all of space to fill,
Like boundless Igdrasil
That has the stars for fruit.

But something at the root
More urgent than that urge

Bids two true leaves emerge,
And now the plant, resigned
To being self-defined
Before it can commerce
With the great universe,
Takes aim at all the sky
And starts to ramify.

D. M. BLACK

Kew Gardens
in memory of Ian A. Black, died January 1971

Distinguished scientist, to whom I greatly defer
(old man, moreover, whom I dearly love),
I walk today in Kew Gardens, in sunlight the colour of
    honey
which flows from the cold autumnal blue of the heavens to
    light these tans and golds,
these ripe corn and leather and sunset colours of the East
    Asian liriodendrons,
of the beeches and maples and plum-trees and the stubborn
    green banks of the holly hedges –
and you walk always beside me, you with your knowledge
    of names
and your clairvoyant gaze, in what for me is sheer
    panorama
seeing the net or web of connectedness. But today it is I who
    speak
(and you are long dead, but it is to you I say it):

'The leaves are green in summer because of chlorophyll
and the flowers are bright to lure the pollinators,
and without remainder (so you have often told me)
these marvellous things that shock the heart the head can
    account for;
but I want to sing an excess which is not so simply
    explainable,
to say that the beauty of the autumn is a redundant beauty,
that the sky had no need to be this particular shade of blue,
nor the maple to die in flames of this particular yellow,

[141]

nor the heart to respond with an ecstasy that does not beget
   children.
I want to say that I do not believe your science
although I believe every word of it, and intend to
   understand it;
that although I rate that unwavering gaze higher than
   almost everything
there is another sense, a hearing, to which I more deeply
   attend.
Thus I withstand and contradict you, I, your child,
who have inherited from you the passion which causes me
   to oppose you.'

NEIL ROLLINSON

My Father Shaving Charles Darwin

As he sinks his backside into the domed
seat of the barber's shop, my father
tips him back like a spaceman to gaze

at the cobwebs whiskered with shavings.
He strokes his fingers through Mr Darwin's
facial hair and tugs, as you might

an implausible stick-on beard.
Well what's it to be, lad?
Only a trim, a bit of a tidy up, says Darwin

settling into the chair.
My father pulls the clippers
out of their box and flicks the switch.

We'll have you looking like a man in next
to no time, my father mutters over the Brylcreem,
can't have you looking like a monkey.

His beard comes off like sparks on a foundry floor.
Need a pair of goggles for this job, he shouts
above the din. He dreams of shaving

the world's heretics clean of their facial hair,
Sigmund Freud, Karl Marx, Fidel Castro; doing his
own little bit for God and for moral decency.

He strops the blade, it runs in furrows
across the man's face, leaving the glass-like purity
that makes my father want to weep.

When the transformation is complete
he takes off the cape and brushes Mr Darwin's neck.
My father's eyes are filled with tears.

He's done a good job, he's humming now,
the tune of 'Jerusalem', stroking the shaven jaws
of Charles Darwin, who sits in his chair, petrified.

Clover Honey

Father first noticed it: 'Upon my Sam,
This soil breeds spinsters! Five miles round, I swear,
Live twenty old maids – not that *I* give a damn,
But Mary and Susan here might have a care.

'Daughters are perishable goods at best;
 At worst – Yes, dear, I *do* know when to stop –
But twenty at church today! Who would have guessed
So rich a shire could raise that blighted crop?'

Susan just giggled; I totted up Father's count:
'Nineteen is what I make it, not twenty, Dad!'
'You've missed our gruesome help here, Sarah Blount,
'Haven't you, girl? Admit it!' – and so I had.

'By God!' – he flourished his carvers in the air –
'She makes my flesh creep. No one asks *my* advice
Of course; but how your mother puts up with her
Passes my – yes, dear! yes, another slice?'

Susan and I discussed it later in bed.
'Father was horrid to laugh; he doesn't *know*!
If I don't marry,' said Sue, 'I'd rather be dead.'
I laughed too: 'Well, we've both some years to go.'

But for all that, I brooded on their lives;
Imagined them as young girls like me or Sue;
Tried to imagine them happy mothers and wives
And wondered what went wrong – though mostly I knew.

Rumour, in country places, rarely leaves
Misfortune a shift or nakedness a clout.
At Tea-cup Time, when Gossip brings home her sheaves,
The skeletons rattle in closets for miles about.

Miss Tabitha and Miss Mildy at the Grange
Had been too high and mighty, people said;
Miss Prue had beauty, but no one thought it strange:
Papa had lost his money. The suitors fled.

Miss Martha had offers too. They had to wait –
A bed-ridden mother – and, as is often the case,
When free to marry, she found it was too late;
Miss Claire's club-foot cancelled that angel face.

Poor, gay Miss Belle never got her man to church;
There was Miss Madeleine, too – but never mind,
Too simple, too yielding: he left her in the lurch.
It's an old story, and people are so unkind.

Miss Sophie was unattractive from the start;
Miss Tetty, of course, had always been a shrew;
But why Miss Constance with her loving heart
Had never married, not even our gossips knew.

Eighteen is an uncompromising age.
Old maids, fag-ends of living, cat-fanciers,
I thought of them with mounting pity and rage
And blamed the order of the universe.

My father's friend – he lived near us in Kent –
A Mr Darwin, used to visit our house,
And when I raged at him in protest, sent
A twinkle at me from his beetle brows:

'Yes, yes, poor things!' he said, 'You have a heart
That does you credit, my dear. But let me say
That the great chain of being has found a part
In Nature's scheme even for them to play.

'You mentioned cats, I think. Each keeps a cat?'
'Good God!', I said, 'they have them by the score!'
'Indeed? Of course, I'm not surprised at that;
But cats catch mice – Well, it's what cats are for.

'Their mistresses at night will put them out
To hunt for field-mice – You begin to see
My drift, perhaps, since as you know, no doubt,
The field-mouse preys upon the bumble-bee.

'These hirsute bees, and they alone, contrive
To fertilize the dark red-clover blooms;
Although it is their smaller cousins who hive
The clover-honey that loads our Kentish combs.

'So when we find – what does the Bible say? –
A land flowing with milk and honey, we do
Not doubt, we naturalists, that there we may
Expect to find old maids a-plenty too.

'The state of single blessedness, you see,
Is not without its talent; indeed, you might
Call spinsters partners of the honey bee
Bringer of life's best gifts, sweetness and light.'

Times change; old maids now in these parts are rare.
That would have made Mr Darwin smile, because
I hear old farmers here in Kent declare
The honey-flow is nothing like it was.

I did not marry, myself. As I recall
I have never had reason to complain of that.
Susan was wed, poor Sue, three times in all;
But now we live together. We keep a cat.

from The Enquiry

How near one Species to the next is join'd,
The due Gradations please a thinking Mind;
And there are Creatures which no Eye can see,
That for a Moment live and breathe like me:
Whom a small Fly in bulk as far exceeds,
As yon tall Cedar does the waving Reeds:
These we can reach – and may we not suppose
There still are Creatures more minute than those.

Wou'd Heav'n permit, and might our Organs bear
To pierce where Comets wave their blazing Hair:
Where other Suns alternate set and rise,
And other Moons light up the chearful Skies:
The ravish'd Soul might still her Search pursue,
Still find new Wonders op'ning on her view:
From thence to Worlds in Miniature descend,
And still press forward, but shou'd find no End:
Where little Forests on a Leaf appear,
And Drops of Dew are mighty Oceans there:
These may have Whales that in their Waters play,
And wanton out their Age of half a Day:
In those small Groves the smaller Birds may sing,
And share like us their Winter and their Spring.

Pluck off yon Acorn from its Parent Bough,
Divide that Acorn in the midst – and now
In its firm Kernel a fair Oak is seen
With spreading Branches of a sprightly Green:
From this young Tree a Kernel might we rend,
There wou'd another its small Boughs extend.

All Matter lives, and shews its Maker's Power;

There's not a Seed but what contains a Flower:
Tho' unobserv'd its secret Beauty lies,
Till we are blest with Microscopick Eyes.
When for blue Plumbs our longing Palate calls,
Or scarlet Cherries that adorn the Walls;
With each plump Fruit we swallow down a Tree,
And so destroy whole Groves that else wou'd be
As large and perfect as those Shades we see.

Behold yon Monster that unwieldy laves
Beneath the Surface of the briny Waves:
Still as he turns, the troubl'd Sea divides;
And rolls in Eddies from his slimy Sides.

Less huge the Dolphin to the Sun displays
His Scales, and in the smoother Ocean plays:
Still less the Herring and round Mackrel sweep
The shallow Tide, nor trust the roaring Deep:
How far by gradual numberless Degrees,
The senseless Oyster is remov'd from these.

Who follows Nature through her mazy Way,
From the mute Insect to the Fount of Day,
(Where now she rises, now her Steps decline)
Has need of Judgment better taught than mine:
But on this Subject we have talk'd too long,
Where grave-fac'd Wisdom may itself be wrong.

Lamarck Elaborated

'The environment creates the organ'

The Greeks were wrong who said our eyes have rays;
Not from these sockets or these sparkling poles
Comes the illumination of our days.
It was the sun that bored these two blue holes.

It was the song of doves begot the ear
And not the ear that first conceived of sound:
That organ bloomed in vibrant atmosphere,
As music conjured Ilium from the ground.

The yielding water, the repugnant stone,
The poisoned berry and the flaring rose
Attired in sense the tactless finger-bone
And set the taste-buds and inspired the nose.

Out of our vivid ambiance came unsought
All sense but that most formidably dim.
The shell of balance rolls in seas of thought.
It was the mind that taught the head to swim.

Newtonian numbers set to cosmic lyres
Whelmed us in whirling worlds we could not know,
And by the imagined floods of our desires
The voice of Sirens gave us vertigo.

Touch

We know she was clever because of her hands.
Hers, the first opposable thumb. Shards of her hip and skull
Suggest she was young, thirteen perhaps,
When the flash flood drowned her. Erect she stood
Lithe as a gymnast, four feet tall,

Our innocent progenitor.
Sleek furred technician of flint and straw.
Here are her knuckle bones.

I know her touch. Though she could easily snap
My wrist, she is gentle in my dream.
She probes my face, scans my arm,
She touches my hand to know me.
Her eyes are grey in the dream, and bright.

Little mother, forgive me.
I wake you for answers in the night
Like any infant. Tell me about touch.
What necessities designed your hands and mine?
Did you kill, carve, gesture to god or gods?
Did the caress shape your hand or your hand the caress?

from The Ascent of Man

And lo, 'mid reeking swarms of earth
    Grim struggling in the primal wood,
A new strange creature hath its birth:
    Wild – stammering – nameless – shameless – nude;
Spurred on by want, held in by fear,
He hides his head in caverns drear.

Most unprotected of earth's kin,
    His fight for life that seems so vain
Sharpens his senses, till within
    The twilight mazes of his brain,
Like embryos within the womb,
Thought pushes feelers through the gloom.

And slowly in the fateful race
    It grows unconscious, till at length
The helpless savage dares to face
    The cave-bear in his grisly strength;
For stronger than its bulky thews
He feels a force that grows with use.

From age to dumb unnumbered age,
    By dim gradations long and slow,
He reaches on from stage to stage,
    Through fear and famine, weal and woe
And, compassed round with danger, still
Prolongs his life by craft and skill.

With cunning hand he shapes the flint,
    He carves the horn with strange device,
He splits the rebel block by dint

Of effort – till one day there flies
A spark of fire from out the stone:
Fire which shall make the world his own.

from Letter to Mary Gisborne

Whoever should behold me now, I wist,
Would think I were a mighty mechanist,
Bent with sublime Archimedean art
To breathe a soul into the iron heart
Of some machine portentous, or strange gin,
Which by the force of figured spells might win
Its way over the sea, and sport therein;
For round the walls are hung dread engines, such
As Vulcan never wrought for Jove to clutch
Ixion or the Titan: – or the quick
Wit of that man of God, St Dominic,
To convince Atheist, Turk, or Heretic,
Or those in philanthropic council met,
Who thought to pay some interest for the debt
They owed to Jesus Christ for their salvation,
By giving a faint foretaste of damnation
To Shakespeare, Sidney, Spenser, and the rest
Who made our land an island of the blest,
When lamp-like Spain, who now relumes her fire
On Freedom's hearth, grew dim with Empire: –
With thumbscrews, wheels, with tooth and spike and jag,
Which fishers found under the utmost crag
Of Cornwall and the storm-encompassed isles,
Where to the sky the rude sea rarely smiles
Unless in treacherous wrath, as on the morn
When the exulting elements in scorn,
Satiated with destroyed destruction, lay
Sleeping in beauty on their mangled prey,
As panthers sleep; – and other strange and dread

Magical forms the brick floor overspread, –
Proteus transformed to metal did not make
More figures, or more strange; nor did he take
Such shapes of unintelligible brass,
Or heap himself in such a horrid mass
Of tin and iron not to be understood;
And forms of unimaginable wood,
To puzzle Tubal Cain and all his brood:
Great screws, and cones, and wheels, and groovèd blocks,
The elements of what will stand the shocks
Of wave and wind and time. – Upon the table
More knacks and quips there be than I am able
To catalogize in this verse of mine: –
A pretty bowl of wood – not full of wine,
But quicksilver; that dew which the gnomes drink
When at their subterranean toil they swink,
Pledging the demons of the earthquake, who
Reply to them in lava – cry halloo!
And call out to the cities o'er their head, –
Roofs, towers, and shrines, the dying and the dead,
Crash through the chinks of earth – and then all quaff
Another rouse, and hold their sides and laugh.
This quicksilver no gnome has drunk – within
The walnut bowl it lies, veinèd and thin,
In colour like the wake of light that stains
The Tuscan deep, when from the moist moon rains
The inmost shower of its white fire – the breeze
Is still – blue Heaven smiles over the pale seas.
And in this bowl of quicksilver – for I
Yield to the impulse of an infancy
Outlasting manhood – I have made to float
A rude idealism of a paper boat: –
A hollow screw with cogs – Henry will know

The thing I mean and laugh at me, – if so
He fears not I should do more mischief. – Next
Lie bills and calculations much perplexed,
With steam-boats, frigates, and machinery quaint
Traced over them in blue and yellow paint.
Then comes a range of mathematical
Instruments, for plans nautical and statical;
A heap of rosin, a queer broken glass
With ink in it; – a china cup that was
What it will never be again, I think, –
A thing from which sweet lips were wont to drink
The liquor doctors rail at – and which I
Will quaff in spite of them – and when we die
We'll toss up who died first of drinking tea,
And cry out, – 'Heads or tails?' where'er we be.
Near that a dusty paint-box, some odd hooks,
A half-burnt match, an ivory block, three books,
Where conic sections, spherics, logarithms,
To great Laplace, from Saunderson and Sims,
Lie heaped in their harmonious disarray
Of figures, – disentangle them who may.
Baron de Tott's Memoirs beside them lie,
And some odd volumes of old chemistry.
Near those a most inexplicable thing,
With lead in the middle – I'm conjecturing
How to make Henry understand; but no –
I'll leave, as Spenser says, with many mo,
This secret in the pregnant womb of time,
Too vast a matter for so weak a rhyme.

THOMAS THORNELY

The Atom

We do not in the least know how to harness the energy locked up in the atoms
of matter. If it could be liberated at will, we should experience a violence
beside which the suddenness of high explosive is gentle and leisurely

Sir O. Lodge

Wake not the imprisoned power that sleeps
Unknown, or dimly guessed, in thee!
Thine awful secret Nature keeps,
And pales, when stealthy science creeps
Towards that beleaguered mystery.

Well may she start and desperate strain,
To thrust the bold besiegers back;
If they that citadel should gain,
What grisly shapes of death and pain
May rise and follow in their track!

The power that warring atoms yield,
Man has to guiltiest purpose turned.
Too soon the wonder was revealed,
Earth flames in one red battle-field;
Could but that lesson be unlearned!

Thy last dread secret, Nature! keep;
Add not to man's tumultuous woes;
Till war and hate are laid to sleep,
Keep those grim forces buried deep,
That in thine atoms still repose.

PETER PORTER

Your Attention Please

The Polar DEW has just warned that
A nuclear rocket strike of
At least one thousand megatons
Has been launched by the enemy
Directly at our major cities.
This announcement will take
Two and a quarter minutes to make,
You therefore have a further
Eight and a quarter minutes
To comply with the shelter
Requirements published in the Civil
Defence Code – section Atomic Attack.
A specially shortened Mass
Will be broadcast at the end
Of this announcement –
Protestant and Jewish services
Will begin simultaneously –
Select your wavelength immediately
According to instructions
In the Defence Code. Do not
Take well-loved pets (including birds)
Into your shelter – they will consume
Fresh air. Leave the old and bed-
ridden, you can do nothing for them.
Remember to press the sealing
Switch when everyone is in
The shelter. Set the radiation
Aerial, turn on the geiger barometer.
Turn off your Television now.

Turn off your radio immediately
The Services end. At the same time
Secure explosion plugs in the ears
Of each member of your family. Take
Down your plasma flasks. Give your children
The pills marked one and two
In the c.d. green container, then put
Them to bed. Do not break
The inside airlock seals until
The radiation All Clear shows
(Watch for the cuckoo in your
Perspex panel), or your District
Touring Doctor rings your bell.
If before this, your air becomes
Exhausted or if any of your family
Is critically injured, administer
The capsules marked 'Valley Forge'
(Red pocket in No. 1 Survival Kit)
For painless death. (Catholics
Will have been instructed by their priests
What to do in this eventuality.)
This announcement is ending. Our President
Has already given orders for
Massive retaliation – it will be
Decisive. Some of us may die.
Remember, statistically
It is not likely to be you.
All flags are flying fully dressed
On Government buildings – the sun is shining.
Death is the least we have to fear.
We are all in the hands of God,
Whatever happens happens by His Will.
Now go quickly to your shelters.

[160]

Tar

The first morning of Three Mile Island: those first
disquieting, uncertain, mystifying hours.
All morning a crew of workmen have been tearing the old
decrepit roof off our building,
and all morning, trying to distract myself, I've been
wandering out to watch them
as they hack away the leaden layers of asbestos paper and
disassemble the disintegrating drains.
After half a night of listening to the news, wondering how
to know a hundred miles downwind
if and when to make a run for it and where, then a coming
bolt awake at seven
when the roofers we've been waiting for since winter sent
their ladders shrieking up our wall,
we still know less than nothing: the utility company
continues making little of the accident,
the slick federal spokesmen still have their evasions in some
semblance of order.
Surely we suspect now we're being lied to, but in the
meantime, there are the roofers,
setting winch-frames, sledging rounds of tar apart, and
there I am, on the curb across, gawking.

I never realized what brutal work it is, how matter-of-factly
and harrowingly dangerous.
The ladders flex and quiver, things skid from the edge, the
materials are bulky and recalcitrant.
When the rusty, antique nails are levered out, their heads
pull off; the underroofing crumbles.

Even the battered little furnace, roaring along as patient as
    a donkey, chokes and clogs,
a dense, malignant smoke shoots up, and someone has to
    fiddle with a cock, then hammer it,
before the gush and stench will deintensify, the dark,
    Dantean broth wearily subside.
In its crucible, the stuff looks bland, like licorice, spill it,
    though, on your boots or coveralls,
it sears, and everything is permeated with it, the furnace
    gunked with burst and half-burst bubbles,
the men themselves so completely slashed and mucked they
    seem almost from another realm, like trolls.
When they take their break, they leave their brooms
    standing at attention in the asphalt pails,
work gloves clinging like Br'er Rabbit to the bitten shafts,
    and they slouch along the precipitous lip,
the enormous sky behind them, the heavy noontime air
    alive with shimmers and mirages.

Sometime in the afternoon I had to go inside: the advent of
    our vigil was upon us.
However much we didn't want to, however little we would
    do about it, we'd understood:
we were going to perish of all this, if not now, then soon, if
    not soon, then someday.
Someday, some final generation, hysterically aswarm
    beneath an atmosphere as unrelenting as rock,
would rue us all, anathematize our earthly comforts, curse
    our surfeits and submissions.
I think I know, though I might rather not, why my roofers
    stay so clear to me and why the rest,
the terror of that time, the reflexive disbelief and distancing,
    all we should hold on to, dims so.

[162]

I remember the president in his absurd protective booties,
    looking absolutely unafraid, the fool.
I remember a woman on the front page glaring across the
    misty Susquehanna at those looming stacks.
But, more vividly, the men, silvered with glitter from the
    shingles, clinging like starlings beneath the eaves.
Even the leftover carats of tar in the gutter, so black they
    seemed to suck the light out of the air.
By nightfall kids had come across them: every sidewalk on
    the block was scribbled with obscenities and hearts.

The Sun Underfoot among the Sundews

An ingenuity too astonishing
to be quite fortuitous is
this bog full of sundews, sphagnum-
lined and shaped like a teacup.
                              A step
down and you're into it; a
wilderness swallows you up:
ankle-, then knee-, then midriff-
to-shoulder-deep in wetfooted
understory, an overhead
spruce-tamarack horizon hinting
you'll never get out of here.
                              But the sun
among the sundews, down there,
is so bright, an underfoot
webwork of carnivorous rubies,
a star-warm thick as the gnats
they're set to catch, delectable
double-faced cockleburs, each
hair-tip a sticky mirror
afire with sunlight, a million
of them and again a million,
each mirror a trap set to
unhand unbelieving,
                              that either
a First Cause said once, 'Let there
be sundews,' and there were, or they've
made their way here unaided

other than by that backhand, round-
about refusal to assume responsibility
known as Natural Selection.

But the sun

underfoot is so dazzling
down there among the sundews,
there is so much light
in the cup that, looking,
you start to fall upward.

from Killing Time

Why don't we start again from the top, from the head:
  dream up a new cult, think of a new force.
Time collects. Time passes, but not with the tread
  of footprints in sand or tyres along a road
or a train on the East Coast line, passing a junction box.
  Time collects, accumulates, gathers together,
remains to be seen. Time thickens, coagulates, clots;
  what lies at your feet is its sediment,
piled from the core to the surface, forming the ground.
  Time builds up in layers: up there
is the clean, unknowable future waiting to rain down
  or fall out, waiting to drop. The present,
the here and now, extends from our minds to our toes,
  from the crowned heads to the down-at-heel,
from verrucas to brain tumours, haloes and frontal lobes,
  from our snoods to our air-cushioned soles.
But underground is the past. Below stairs –
  that's where dust and bone
and pollen and skin and rust and soot and fibre and hair
  and splinter and soil are packed hard,
becoming stone, becoming rock, becoming earth.
  And not just things we can measure
and weigh, items of proof, material worth,
  but sounds and visions,
echoes and views – they lie here in the stone,
  jammed into silence
and blackness by time, by its billion billion tons,
  time laying down its load.

The great geology of time. The gravity of loss.
　　And memory lies here too.
Memory – the glue of time, bonding it close,
　　the gel that splices
one split second to the next, the gum that sets the past
　　in solid form, binding it shut,
holding it monumentally hard and fast.
　　So history can be opened again,
but not by force. Plastic explosive will fail
　　to worm time from its shell;
hard labour, hammer blow, pulverization, blade and file,
　　reduction of solid form to its powdered state
will not release time, neither will high-voltage connections,
　　magnets, particular wavelengths of light,
nor pinning-down under powerful lenses, looking at
　　　　　　　　　　　　　　　sections slice
　　by slice, or baking hard in a kiln.
Time will not be extracted like ore
　　from its mother-rock, like mercury
from cinnabar, or drilled from the planet's core.
　　Only water will work.
Water that makes its way down, reaches back to the first.
　　Water which mimics the action of time,
which makes for the lowest point; that is its task, its thirst.
　　The world over, water is working
its trick: conjuring up whatever is unseen and unsung.
　　Atoms of history boil up
into the air, vaporize into the lungs.
　　Hold it there. You are keeping
yourself in breath with the dates and figures and facts
　　and lives and losses and loves
of a history smothered by dust. You are breathing the past.
　　Make it real again, because

[167]

this is the cycle to which we are all born.
    We journeyed ashore
to set the past free, to release the secret of time from stone,
    uncurl the stubborn fist of what is gone,
to flood the rocks that hold the limited supply of time,
    to irrigate memory
and float the great, revolving permanence of humankind.
    Look down at your feet, which are fish.
Imagine everything locked in time's keep,
    everything buried, enshrined, encrypted, encoded,
                              entombed
in sleep. Now, bring back the dead. Breathe deep.

Dear Isaac Newton
for Michael Cuddihy

Your famous apple
Is still falling.

Your red, ripe,
Properly notarized
Old Testament apple.

(The night's denseness is no help.)

All that we expostulated
To cause her to stay up there.

All the spells and curses
To hold and bind,
To enchant permanently
In the realm of seraphim.

She appeared to dilly dally, to consider.
She was already empyreal,
Ruled by some other reckoning,
When she shuddered and fell.

(The famous *malus pumila*.)

How heavy, how grave she grows
With each headlong instant
As though the seeds inside her
Were a catch of celestial razor-chips.

(Is she suffering for us, Isaac,
In some still incomprehensible way?)

Soon she'll rest at our feet.
Soon she'll strike the earth angrily,
For the earth's a pool table
The gravediggers have hewn with their spades.

Quickly then!
Make your bed,
Set your pillow on the apple
While she still spins.

Understand coldly
Impartially,
There's time only
For a single thought,

A single conjecture
As the bones rejoice in the earth,
As the maggots romp
In the Sunday roast . . .

(The famous apple up there.)

O she's falling lawfully,
But isn't she now
Perhaps even more mysterious
Than when she first started?

And wasn't that one of her
Prize worms
We saw crawling off
Into the unthinkable?

ROALD HOFFMAN

Giving In

At 1.4 million atmospheres
xenon, a gas, goes metallic.
Between squeezed single-bevel
diamond anvils jagged bits
of graphite shot with a YAG
laser form spherules. No one
has seen liquid carbon. Try
to imagine that dense world
between ungiving diamonds
as the pressure mounts, and
the latticework of a salt
gives, nucleating at defects
a shift to a tighter order.
Try to see graphite boil. Try
to imagine a hand, in a press,
in a cellar in Buenos Aires,
a low-tech press, easily
turned with one hand, easily
cracking a finger in another
man's hand, the jagged bone
coming through, to be crushed
again. No. Go back, up, up
like the deep diver with
a severed line, up, quickly,
to the orderly world of ruby
and hydrogen at 2.5 megabar,
the hydrogen coloring near

metallization, but you hear
the scream in the cellar, don't
you, and the diver rises too fast.

The Scale of Intensity

1) Not felt. Smoke still rises vertically. In sensitive individuals, déjà vu, mild amnesia. Sea like a mirror.

2) Detected by persons at rest or favourably placed, i.e. in upper floors, hammocks, cathedrals, etc. Leaves rustle.

3) Light sleepers wake. Glasses chink. Hairpins, paperclips display slight magnetic properties. Irritability. Vibration like passing of light trucks.

4) Small bells ring. Small increase in surface tension and viscosity of certain liquids. Domestic violence. Furniture overturned.

5) Heavy sleepers wake. Pendulum clocks stop. Public demonstrations. Large flags fly. Vibration like passing of heavy trucks.

6) Large bells ring. Bookburning. Aurora visible in daylight hours. Unprovoked assaults on strangers. Glassware broken. Loose tiles fly from roof.

7) Weak chimneys broken off at roofline. Waves on small ponds, water turbid with mud. Unprovoked assaults on neighbours. Large static charges built up on windows, mirrors, television screens.

8) Perceptible increase in weight of stationary objects: books, cups, pens heavy to lift. Fall of stucco and some masonry. Systematic rape of women and young girls. Sand craters. Cracks in wet ground.

9) Small trees uprooted. Bathwater drains in reverse vortex. Wholesale slaughter of religious and ethnic minorities. Conspicuous cracks in ground. Damage to reservoirs and underground pipelines.

10) Large trees uprooted. Measurable tide in puddles, teacups, etc. Torture and rape of small children. Irreparable damage to foundations. Rails bend. Sand shifts horizontally on beaches.

11) Standing impossible. Widespread self-mutilation. Corposant visible on pylons, lampposts, metal railings. Waves seen on ground surface. Most bridges destroyed.

12) Damage total. Movement of hour hand perceptible. Large rock masses displaced. Sea white.

Earthling

You have probably come across
those scales in planetariums
that tell you how much you
would weigh on other planets.

You have noticed the fat ones
lingering on the Mars scale
and the emaciated slowing up
the line for Neptune.

As a creature of average weight,
I fail to see the attraction.

Imagine squatting in the wasteland
of Pluto, all five tons of you,
or wandering around Mercury
wondering what to do next with your ounce.

How much better to step onto
the simple bathroom scale,
a happy earthling feeling
the familiar ropes of gravity,

157 pounds standing soaking wet
a respectful distance from the sun.

Westering
in California

I sit under Rand McNally's
'Official Map of the Moon' –
The colour of frogskin,
Its enlarged pores held

Open and one called
'Pitiscus' at eye level –
Recalling the last night
In Donegal, my shadow

Neat upon the whitewash
From her bony shine,
The cobbles of the yard
Lit pale as eggs.

Summer had been a free fall
Ending there,
The empty amphitheatre
Of the west. Good Friday

We had started out
Past shopblinds drawn on the afternoon,
Cars stilled outside still churches,
Bikes tilting to a wall;

We drove by,
A dwindling interruption
As clappers smacked
On a bare altar

And congregations bent
To the studded crucifix.
What nails dropped out that hour?
Roads unreeled, unreeled

Falling light as casts
Laid down
On shining waters.
Under the moon's stigmata

Six thousand miles away,
I imagine untroubled dust,
A loosening gravity,
Christ weighing by his hands.

'I am like a slip of comet'

– I am like a slip of comet,
Scarce worth discovery, in some corner seen
Bridging the slender difference of two stars,
Come out of space, or suddenly engender'd
By heady elements, for no man knows;
But when she sights the sun she grows and sizes
And spins her skirts out, while her central star
Shakes its cocooning mists; and so she comes
To fields of light; millions of travelling rays
Pierce her; she hangs upon the flame-cased sun,
And sucks the light as full as Gideon's fleece:
But then her tether calls her; she falls off,
And as she dwindles shreds her smock of gold
Between the sistering planets, till she comes
To single Saturn, last and solitary;
And then she goes out into the cavernous dark.
So I go out: my little sweet is done:
I have drawn heat from this contagious sun:
To not ungentle death now forth I run.

ANNA LAETITIA BARBAULD

from A Summer Evening's Meditation

                              Seiz'd in thought
On fancy's wild and roving wing I sail,
From the green borders of the peopled earth,
And the pale moon, her duteous fair attendant;
From solitary Mars; from the vast orb
Of Jupiter, whose huge gigantic bulk
Dances in ether like the lightest leaf;
To the dim verge, the suburbs of the system,
Where chearless Saturn 'midst her watry moons
Girt with a lucid zone, majestic sits
In gloomy grandeur; like an exil'd queen
Amongst her weeping handmaids: fearless thence
I launch into the trackless deeps of space,
Where, burning round, ten thousand suns appear,
Of elder beam; which ask no leave to shine
Of our terrestrial star, nor borrow light
From the proud regent of our scanty day;
Sons of the morning, first born of creation,
And only less than him who marks their track,
And guides their fiery wheels. Here must I stop,
Or is their aught beyond? What hand unseen
Impels me onward thro' the glowing orbs
Of habitable nature; far remote,
To the dread confines of eternal night,
To solitudes of vast unpeopled space,
The desarts of creation, wide and wild;
Where embryo systems and unkindled suns
Sleep in the womb of chaos; fancy droops,
And thought astonish'd stops her bold career.

Letter I

You were amused to find you too could fear
'The eternal silence of the infinite spaces,'
That net-work without fish, that mere
Extended idleness, those pointless places
Who, being possibilized to bear faces,
Yours and the light from it, up-buoyed,
Even of the galaxies are void.

I approve, myself, dark spaces between stars;
All privacy's their gift; they carry glances
Through gulfs; and as for messages (thus Mars'
Reknown for wisdom their wise tact enhances,
Hanged on the thread of radio advances)
For messages, they are a wise go-between,
And say what they think common-sense has seen.

Only, have we space, common-sense in common,
A tribe whose life-blood is our sacrament,
Physics or metaphysics for your showman,
For my physician in this banishment?
Too non-Euclidean predicament.
Where is that darkness that gives light its place?
Or where such darkness as would hide your face?

Our jovial sun, if he avoids exploding
(These times are critical), will cease to grin,
Will lose your circumambient foreboding;
Loose the full radiance his mass can win
While packed with mass holds all that radiance in;
Flame far too hot not to seem utter cold
And hide a tumult never to be told.

LES MURRAY

The Man with the Hoe

Thinking about air conditioning's Willis Carrier
who also won the West, I am turning
earth in on a long potato drill,
which is like folding history down on trench lines

of unnumbered mild faces. The day
is overcast, with rain pricking the air
and us to hurry, plying our hoes along this promontory
above Horses Creek. The channel-billed cuckoo

shouts, flying, and the drug squad helicopter
comes singing *I'll spot it, your pot plot.*
O lord of love, look from above
sang the churches, but what looks down

from beyond the sky now's the television
of a spy satellite, feeding the coordinates
of today's cloud nations into spinning
tapes for the updating screens of judgement.

The Lord of love is in decay. Relievedly.
He's in worn flanks of stonework, in weathering
garden posts, in the survival of horses,
in humans' long survival after mating, in ticky tacky

buildings that mean the builders were paid properly
and not always by magnates. He is more apparent
in the idea, verandahs and visitings of a hospital
than the stunning theatre. More in surrounds than the
  centre

[181]

where he is ground against, love versus love, he lives
in the bantering pauses. The pattern of love's also
behind our continuing to cover these potatoes
which, by her mercy, also look like potatoes.

Warmth makes cool. The mystery of refrigeration –
but now three fighter aircraft distil out
of the north hills, fast, ahead of their enormous
collapse of sound. Cloud resorbs them. As in the bra ad

the heart lifts and separates, shrivelled with exultation
that is the angel of history: a boy bored rigid
with farmwork sights along a noble light-draining
sword blade held at the level of his mouth.

Cold. Burning cold. The old tremendous imagery
of the Judgement recycles cold, in a bitter age
where love is passion, and passion is the action.
Who could trust a God of love, now we have seen

the love that ignites stars, and ourselves possess such
      ignition?
Who would trust a god on heat nearer than the stars?
Who can trust heat, that may now freeze the planet?
Who can trust coldness, matrix of utter heat?

We cry for cool, because we long for warmth.
When the fighters grow obsolete, and their pipes cool,
warmth reinvests them. It seems a reversing cycle.
Let the Lord be warm and cool, and judgement be

a flower I'm not good enough to unfold yet,
as I stitch down this earth, and my uncle comes driving
his skittish young tractor over our holey paddock,
my uncle the ex-smoker – not pot: we're older than the pot
      lot –

who starts conversations with a ruminative ahaanh,
not *aha! I've caught you!* A shyer reconnecting ahaanh
warm from past meetings. This is among my people
whom I do understand, but not before they speak.

PAUL MULDOON

The Electric Orchard

The early electric people had domesticated the wild ass.
They knew all about falling off.
Occasionally, they would have fallen out of the trees.
Climbing again, they had something to prove
To their neighbours. And they did have neighbours.
The electric people lived in villages
Out of their need of security and their constant hunger.
Together they would divert their energies

To neutral places. Anger to the banging door,
Passion to the kiss.
And electricity to earth. Having stolen his thunder
From an angry god, through the trees
They had learned to string his lightning.
The women gathered random sparks into their aprons,
A child discovered the swing
Among the electric poles. Taking everything as given,

The electric people were confident, hardly proud.
They kept fire in a bucket,
Boiled water and dry leaves in a kettle, watched the lid
By the blue steam lifted and lifted.
So that, where one of the electric people happened to fall,
It was accepted as an occupational hazard.
There was something necessary about the thing. The
    North Wall
Of the Eiger was notorious for blizzards,

If one fell there his neighbour might remark, Bloody fool.
All that would have been inappropriate,
Applied to the experienced climber of electric poles.

[184]

I have achieved this great height?
No electric person could have been that proud,
Thirty or forty feet. Perhaps not that,
If the fall happened to be broken by the roof of a shed.
The belt would burst, the call be made,

The ambulance arrive and carry the faller away
To hospital with a scream.
There and then the electric people might invent the
    railway,
Just watching the lid lifted by the steam.
Or decide that all laws should be based on that of gravity,
Just thinking of the faller fallen.
Even then they were running out of things to do and see.
Gradually, they introduced legislation

Whereby they nailed a plaque to every last electric pole.
They would prosecute any trespassers.
The high up, singing and live fruit liable to shock or kill
Were forbidden. Deciding that their neighbours
And their neighbours' innocent children ought to be
    stopped
For their own good, they threw a fence
Of barbed wire round the electric poles. None could
    describe
Electrocution, falling, the age of innocence.

from Of the Pythagorean Philosophy

'Time was, when we were sowed, and just began,
From some few fruitful drops, the promise of a man;
Then nature's hand (fermented as it was)
Moulded to shape the soft, coagulated mass;
And when the little man was fully formed,
The breathless embryo with a spirit warmed;
But when the mother's throes begin to come,
The creature, pent within the narrow room,
Breaks his blind prison, pushing to repair
His stifled breath, and draw the living air;
Cast on the margin of the world he lies,
A helpless babe, but by instinct he cries.
He next essays to walk, but, downward pressed
On four feet imitates his brother beast:
By slow degrees he gathers from the ground
His legs, and to the rolling chair is bound;
Then walks alone; a horseman now become,
He rides a stick, and travels round the room:
In time he vaunts among his youthful peers,
Strong-boned, and strung with nerves, in pride of years,
He runs with mettle his first merry stage,
Maintains the next, abated of his rage,
But manages his strength, and spares his age.
Heavy the third, and stiff, he sinks apace,
And though 'tis downhill all, but creeps along the race.
Now sapless on the verge of death he stands,
Contemplating his former feet, and hands;
And Milo-like, his slackened sinews sees,

And withered arms, once fit to cope with Hercules,
Unable now to shake, much less to tear the trees. [. . .]

'Nor those, which elements we call, abide,
Nor to this figure, nor to that are tied:
For this eternal world is said of old
But four prolific principles to hold,
Four different bodies; two to heaven ascend,
And other two down to the centre tend.
Fire first with wings expanded mounts on high,
Pure, void of weight, and dwells in upper sky;
Then air, because unclogged in empty space
Flies after fire, and claims the second place;
But weighty water as her nature guides,
Lies on the lap of earth; and mother earth subsides.
'All things are mixed of these, which all contain,
And into these are all resolved again:
Earth rarefies to dew; expanded more,
The subtle dew in air begins to soar;
Spreads as she flies, and weary of her name
Extenuates still, and changes into flame;
Thus having by degrees perfection won,
Restless they soon untwist the web they spun,
And fire begins to lose her radiant hue,
Mixed with gross air, and air descends to dew;
And dew condensing, does her form forego,
And sinks, a heavy lump of earth below.
'Thus are their figures never at a stand,
But changed by nature's innovating hand;
All things are altered, nothing is destroyed,
The shifted scene, for some new show employed. [. . .]

'But this by sure experiment we know
That living creatures from corruption grow:

[187]

Hide in a hollow pit a slaughtered steer,
Bees from his putrid bowels will appear;
Who like their parents haunt the fields, and bring
Their honey harvest home, and hope another spring.
The warlike steed is multiplied we find,
To wasps and hornets of the warrior kind.
Cut from a crab his crooked claws and hide
The rest in earth, a scorpion thence will glide
And shoot his sting, his tail in circles tossed
Refers the limbs his backward father lost.
And worms, that stretch on leaves their filmy loom,
Crawl from their bags, and butterflies become.
E'en slime begets the frog's loquacious race:
Short of their feet at first, in little space
With arms and legs endued, long leaps they take,
Raised on their hinder part, and swim the lake,
And waves repel: for nature gives their kind
To that intent, a length of legs behind.
  'The cubs of bears, a living lump appear,
When whelped, and no determined figure wear.
Their mother licks them into shape, and gives
As much of form, as she herself receives.
  'The grubs from their sexangular abode
Crawl out unfinished, like the maggot's brood,
Trunks without limbs; till time at leisure brings
The thighs they wanted, and their tardy wings.
  'The bird who draws the car of Juno, vain
Of her crowned head, and of her starry train;
And he that bears the artillery of Jove,
The strong-pounced eagle, and the billing dove;
And all the feathered kind, who could suppose
(But that from sight, the surest sense he knows)
They from the included yolk, not ambient white, arose.

'There are who think the marrow of a man,
Which in the spine, while he was living, ran;
When dead, the pith corrupted will become
A snake, and hiss within the hollow tomb. [. . .]

'A wonder more amazing would we find?
The hyena shows it, of a double kind,
Varying the sexes in alternate years,
In one begets, and in another bears.
The thin chameleon fed with air, receives
The colour of the thing to which he cleaves.
'India when conquered, on the conquering god
For planted vines the sharp-eyed lynx bestowed,
Whose urine shed, before it touches earth,
Congeals in air, and gives to gems their birth.
So coral soft, and white in ocean's bed,
Comes hardened up in air, and glows with red.
'All changing species should my song recite,
Before I ceased, would change the day to night. [. . .]

'And therefore I conclude; whatever lies
In earth, or flits in air, or fills the skies,
All suffer change, and we, that are of soul
And body mixed, are members of the whole.
Then, when our sires, or grandsires, shall forsake
The forms of men, and brutal figures take,
Thus housed, securely let their spirits rest,
Nor violate thy father in the beast.
Thy friend, thy brother, any of thy kin,
Is none of these, yet there's a man within:
O spare to make a Thyestean meal,
To enclose his body, and his soul expel.
'Ill customs by degrees to habits rise,
Ill habits soon become exalted vice:

[189]

What more advance can mortals make in sin
So near perfection, who with blood begin?
Deaf to the calf that lies beneath the knife,
Looks up, and from her butcher begs her life;
Deaf to the harmless kid, that ere he dies
All methods to procure thy mercy tries,
And imitates in vain thy children's cries.
Where will he stop, who feeds with household bread,
Then eats the poultry which before he fed?
Let plough thy steers; that when they lose their breath
To nature, not to thee, they may impute their death.
Let goats for food their loaded udders lend,
And sheep from winter-cold thy sides defend;
But neither springes, nets, nor snares employ,
And be no more ingenious to destroy.
Free as in air, let birds on earth remain,
Nor let insidious glue their wings constrain;
Nor opening hounds the trembling stag affright,
Nor purple feathers intercept his flight:
Nor hooks concealed in baits for fish prepare,
Nor lines to heave them twinkling up in air.
    'Take not away the life you cannot give;
For all things have an equal right to live.
Kill noxious creatures, where 'tis sin to save;
This only just prerogative we have:
But nourish life with vegetable food,
And shun the sacrilegious taste of blood.'

GEOFFREY LEHMANN

Not Yet Found

I chose the name Spring Forest
and I've yet to find the spring.

Some unfinished equations
are the closest I've come
to the puzzle of why I'm here.

There is a book before our eyes –
the night sky of the universe.
Galileo saw its language was mathematics.
A cricket's encrypted love song,
light from an ancient star
are mathematical messages
arriving in sultry air.

Imaginary and complex numbers
allow life to reproduce itself
endlessly and intricately
without repetition –
the elusive algorithms of a summer night.

DEREK MAHON

Mt Gabriel

As if planted there by giant golfers in the skies,
White in the gloaming, last before New Brunswick,
The geodesic domes have left their caves
To sit out in the summer sunset. Angels
Beamed at Namancos and Bayona, sick
With exile, they yearn homeward now, their eyes
Tuned to the ultramarine, first-star-pierced dark
Reflected on the dark, incoming waves –
Who, aliens, burnt-out meteorites, time capsules,
Are here for ever now as intermediaries
Between the big bang and our scattered souls.

ANONYMOUS

'Thulë, the period of Cosmography'

Thulë, the period of Cosmography,
  Doth vaunt of Hecla, whose sulphureous fire
Doth melt the frozen clime and thaw the sky;
  Trinacrian Aetna's flames ascend not higher.
These things seem wondrous, yet more wondrous I,
Whose heart with fear doth freeze, with love doth fry.

The Andalusian merchant, that returns
  Laden with cochineal and China dishes,
Reports in Spain how strangely Fogo burns
  Amidst an ocean full of flying fishes.
These things seem wondrous, yet more wondrous I,
Whose heart with fear doth freeze, with love doth fry.

About Planck Time

Once upon a time, way back in the infinitesimal
First fraction of a second attending our creation,
A tiny drop containing all of it, all energy
And all its guises, burst upon the scene,
Exploding out of nothing into everything
Virtually instantaneously, the way our thoughts
Leap eagerly to occupy the abhorrent void.
Once, say ten or twenty billion years ago,
In Planck time, in no time at all, the veil
Available to our perceptions was flung out
Over space at such a rate the mere imagination
Cannot keep up, so rapidly the speed of light
Lags miraculously behind, producing a series
Of incongruities that has led our curiosity,
Like Ariadne's thread, through the dim labyrinth
Of our conclusions to the place of our beginning.
In Planck time, everything that is was spread so thin
That all distance is enormous, between each star,
Between subatomic particles, so that we are composed
Almost entirely of emptiness, so that what separates
This world, bright ball floating in its midnight blue,
From the irrefutable logic of no world at all
Has no more substance than the traveller's dream,
So that nothing can be said for certain except
That sometime, call it Planck time, it will all just
Disappear, a parlor trick, a rabbit back in its hat,
Will all go up in a flash of light, abracadabra,
An idea that isn't being had anymore.

Zoom!

It begins as a house, an end terrace
in this case
    but it will not stop there. Soon it is
an avenue
    which cambers arrogantly past the Mechanics' Institute,
turns left
    at the main road without even looking
and quickly it is
    a town with all four major clearing banks,
a daily paper
    and a football team pushing for promotion.

On it goes, oblivious of the Planning Acts,
the green belts,
    and before we know it it is out of our hands:
city, nation,
    hemisphere, universe, hammering out in all directions
until suddenly,
    mercifully, it is drawn aside through the eye
of a black hole
    and bulleted into a neighbouring galaxy, emerging
smaller and smoother
    than a billiard ball but weighing more than Saturn.

People stop me in the street, badger me
in the check-out queue
    and ask 'What is this, this that is so small
and so very smooth

but whose mass is greater than the ringed planet?'
It's just words
   I assure them. But they will not have it.

Notes

7 The cosmology of *Orchestra* (1596) is Ptolemaic, though Copernicus' theory (1543) that the earth revolves around the sun is acknowledged in passing.

16 Lucy Hutchinson was born in the Tower of London, where her mother reputedly helped Sir Walter Ralegh to finance his chemical experiments. A Puritan, she translated selectively from Lucretius; her poems were unpublished.

24 William Harvey (1578–1657) discovered the circulation of the blood.

31 The illness of 'the spleen' was a complaint similar to what we call depression today. Richard Lower (1631–91) was an outstanding medical scientist whose investigations included the anatomy of the brain.

38 The world-view of Donne's love poems, written in the 1590s, is Ptolemaic; 'Of the Progress of the Soul' (1612) shows his awareness of the new learning and his antipathy towards it.

40 The law flouted in 'The Lover' is the Second Law of Thermodynamics, which gives time its irreversible 'forward' direction.

50 Olbers' Paradox concerns the fact that the sky is dark at night even though it is full of stars. The number of neurons in the brain is roughly the same as the number of stars in the Milky Way.

65 The medieval theory of sound was widely known from Boethius' treatise on music; Chaucer is also thinking of the fart.

74 Cowper based his poem on a newspaper report and wrote it originally in Latin.

80 *Jubilate Agno* was mostly written during Smart's years in an asylum and was not published until 1939.

94 Richard Leigh wrote poems exploring the new physics of sight and sound and published one book, *Poems* (1675).

97 Edward Taylor was a seventeenth-century American divine whose poems were discovered in manuscript in 1937.

99 Sir Arthur Eddington (1882–1944), the founder of astrophysics, was also a keen popularizer. In a famous passage he explained how the scientist sees a table, and its constituent atoms, as mostly empty space.

108 Marie Curie died of leukaemia, very likely as result of her years of exposure to radiation; her notebooks are still radioactive.

118 Roald Hoffman received the Nobel Prize for Chemistry in 1981.

123 A Möbius strip is made by twisting a rectangular length of card once and joining the ends; it then has one continuous surface. The poem's other mathematical terms refer to shapes with similarly unexpected properties.

126 Gödel's Theorem (1931) requires that even the most rigorous systems, like those of mathematics and logic, must be either incomplete or inconsistent. Baron Münchhausen is the hero of picaresque stories by Raspe.

149 Mary Leapor worked as a servant-girl in Northhamptonshire; she had a personal library of 'about sixteen or seventeen single Volumes' that included the poems of Pope.

151 Jean Baptiste Lamarck (1774–1829) believed that living things adapted to their environment and then passed on these acquired characteristics to their descendants. This is a faster and more appealing mechanism for evolution than Darwin's principle of natural selection, but it isn't true.

161 A near-disastrous nuclear accident occurred at the Three Mile Island power station in 1979.

179 Anna Laetitia Barbauld belonged to a notable group of dissenters that included Joseph Priestley, who in 1774 isolated oxygen.

186 The Discourse of Pythagoras, in the last book of Ovid's *Metamorphoses*, was also admired by Newton.

192 Mt Gabriel in the south-west of Ireland has two giant ball-like structures, presumably 'listening posts', near its summit.

194 Planck Time (after Max Planck, 1858–1947, the founder of
quantum mechanics) is the smallest possible measurement of
time. It is equal to 10^{-43} seconds. Nothing can happen in a
shorter time. The universe was already this old when it came
into existence and its entire mass was packed into a minute
space of explosive density.

Acknowledgements

The editors and publishers gratefully acknowledge permission to reprint copyright material in this book as follows:

FLEUR ADCOCK: from *Poems 1960–2000*, published by Bloodaxe books, 2000, reprinted by permission of the publisher. SIMON ARMITAGE: from *Zoom!* published by Bloodaxe Books, 1989, reprinted by permission of the publisher; from *Killing Time*, reprinted by permission of Faber and Faber Ltd. W. H. AUDEN: from *Collected Poems*, © 1962 by W. H. Auden, published by Faber and Faber Ltd and reproduced by permission of the publisher; reprinted in Canada by permission of Random House Inc. D. M. BLACK: from *Selected Poems 1964–1987*, published by Polygon, 1991, reprinted by permission of Edinburgh University Press. AMY CLAMPITT: from *Collected Poems*, published by Faber and Faber Ltd, reprinted by permission of the publisher. ALISON DEMING: from *Science and Other Poems*, © 1994, reprinted by permission of Louisiana State University Press. MICHAEL DONAGHY from *Shibboleth*, first published by Oxford University Press, 1988, reprinted by permission of the author. WILLIAM EMPSON: from *Collected Poems*, published by Chatto & Windus, 1962, reprinted by permission of the publisher. ROBERT FROST: from *The Poetry of Robert Frost*, published by Holt Pinehurst and Winston, 1967, reprinted by permission of the editor, Edward Connery Latham, the Estate of Robert Frost and the publisher Jonathan Cape. ALICE FULTON: from *Sensual Math*, copyright © Alice Fulton, reprinted by permission of W. W. Norton & Company. LAVINIA GREEENLAW: from *Night Photograph*, © Lavinia Greenlaw, 1993, reprinted by permission of Faber and Faber Ltd. PHILIP GROSS: from *The Cat's Whisker*, reprinted by permission of Faber and Faber Ltd. SEAMUS HEANEY: from *Wintering Out*, reprinted by permission of Faber and Faber Ltd. ROALD HOFFMAN: from *Gaps and Verses*, © Roald Hoffman 1990, reprinted by permission of the University Press of Florida. MIROSLAV HOLUB: from *Poems Before and After: Collected English Translations*, translated by Ewald Osers, published by Bloodaxe Books, 1990, reprinted by permission of the publisher. TED HUGHES: from *Flowers and Insects*, reprinted by permission of

Index of Poets

Index of First Lines

[206]